abc's of
SILICON CONTROLLED
RECTIFIERS

by **ALLAN LYTEL**

HOWARD W. SAMS & CO., INC.
THE BOBBS-MERRILL CO., INC.
INDIANAPOLIS · KANSAS CITY · NEW YORK

FIRST EDITION

SEVENTH PRINTING—1974

International Standard Book Number: 0-672-20124-0
Library of Congress Catalog Card Number: 65-27211

Preface

Semiconductors have gradually worked their way into electronics until they almost dominate the field. The first practical units to be developed were made of two layers of semiconductor material. These were rectifiers—first of small signals and later, as production techniques improved, of almost unlimited currents and voltages. A three-layer device, the transistor, was next. As an amplifier and a switch, it has replaced many types of electron tubes and made possible a miniaturization of circuits far beyond that thought possible a few years ago.

The silicon controlled rectifier (SCR), consisting of four layers of semiconductor material with leads attached to three of them, represents the next stage of development. The SCR combines the actions of both rectifiers and transistors in a single unit. As a rectifier, its switching action converts alternating current to direct current. As an amplifier, it can use a signal in the microampere region to turn on and off currents of a hundred amperes or more. Taken as a whole, it is a high-speed switch capable of handling large currents and voltages.

SCR's are being used today. In industrial equipment they are replacing thyratrons in the controls for electric motors and production machinery. They are also being incorporated into electric irons, mixers, motor-driven hand tools, and countless other items that are a part of everyday living. Understanding SCR's is becoming necessary for everyone in technical fields.

This book is written to provide a basic knowledge of SCR's—how they work, what they can do, and where they can be used. Using the background it provides, you will be able to take maximum advantage of the more technical literature available on the subject.

ALLAN LYTEL

Contents

1

Basic Principles

The invention of the transistor less than twenty years ago marked the beginning of a new age; since that time, electronic tubes have gradually been made obsolete as semiconductor technology has advanced. Not only do the new devices replace the older tubes, but they are also able to function in situations where tubes cannot be used. In addition, the small size of semiconductors makes possible complex circuitry that would have been impossible with the larger tubes. Semiconductors are rapidly dominating the electronic field.

The silicon controlled rectifier—usually referred to as an SCR—is one of the family of semiconductors that includes transistors and diodes. A drawing of an SCR and its schematic representation is shown in Fig. 1-1; note the similarity. Not all SCR's use the case shown, but this is typical of most of the high-power units.

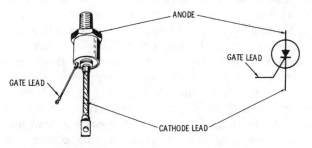

(A) A high-power unit.   *(B) The schematic symbol.*

Fig. 1-1. Silicon controlled rectifier.

Although it is not the same as either a diode or a transistor, the SCR combines features of both, opening up many new fields of application for semiconductors. Circuits now utilizing transistors or rectifier diodes may be greatly improved in some cases through the use of SCR's, and many additional circuits can now be converted to semiconductors due to their unique properties.

The basic purpose of the SCR is to function as a switch that can turn on or off small or large amounts of power. It performs this function with no moving parts that wear out and no points that require replacing. There can be a tremendous power gain in the SCR; a very small triggering current in some units is able to switch several hundred amperes without exceeding its rated abilities. The SCR can often replace much slower and larger mechanical switches. It even has many advantages over its more complex and larger electronic-tube equivalent, the thyratron.

The SCR is an extremely fast switch. It is difficult (and frequently undesirable) to cycle a mechanical switch several hundred times a minute; yet, some SCR's now available can be switched 25,000 times a second. It takes just microseconds (millionths of a second) to turn on or off these units. This switching ability opens another important field of applications—control of power. By varying the duty cycle of a switch (the time on compared to the time off), the amount of power flowing through the switch can be regulated. Since most devices can operate on pulses of power (alternating current is a special form of alternating positive and negative pulses), the SCR can be used readily in control applications.

The SCR's are new, and at the present time much of the work being done with them is experimental or developmental. Commercial possibilities being investigated include motor-speed control for all sorts of devices from drill presses and metal lathes to saws; lighting-intensity controls; inverters (providing alternating current from d-c sources); remote switching of power; controlled rectification of alternating current; circuit overload protection; latching relays; computer logic circuits; and many others.

Only in the last few months has the cost of SCR's come down to the point where their full potential of usefulness can be realized. In addition to the commercial electronic control systems mentioned previously, soon they will be appearing in controls for home lighting intensity, food mixers, sewing machines, automobile ignitions, model railroads, toasters, heating units, etc.

SEMICONDUCTOR THEORY

To understand how semiconductors work it is necessary to review briefly the structure of matter. All atoms are made of electrons, protons, and neutrons. Most solid materials are classed, from the standpoint of electrical conductivity, as conductors, semiconductors, or insulators. To be a conductor, the substance must contain some mobile electrons—ones that can move freely between the atoms. These free electrons come only from the valence (outer) orbit of the atom. Physical forces associated with the valence electrons bond adjacent atoms together. The inner electrons, below the valence level, do not normally enter into the conduction process.

Conductivity depends on the number of electrons in the valence orbit. Electron diagrams for three typical elements, aluminum,

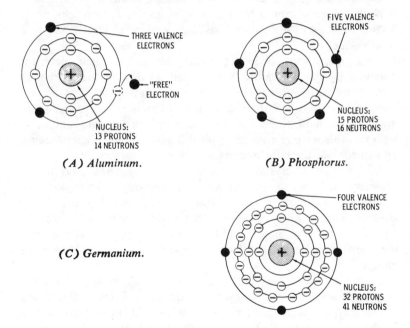

(A) Aluminum.

THREE VALENCE ELECTRONS

"FREE" ELECTRON

NUCLEUS: 13 PROTONS 14 NEUTRONS

(B) Phosphorus.

FIVE VALENCE ELECTRONS

NUCLEUS: 15 PROTONS 16 NEUTRONS

(C) Germanium.

FOUR VALENCE ELECTRONS

NUCLEUS: 32 PROTONS 41 NEUTRONS

Fig. 1-2. Electron configuration of semiconductor materials.

germanium, and phosphorus, are shown in Fig. 1-2. These elements can all be used in semiconductor manufacture. The degree of conductivity is determined as follows:

9

1. Atoms with fewer than four valence electrons are good conductors.
2. Atoms with more than four valence electrons are poor conductors.
3. Atoms with four valence electrons are semiconductors.

Aluminum, which has three valence electrons, is shown in Fig. 1-2A. When there are less than four valence electrons they are loosely held so that at least one electron per atom is normally free; hence, aluminum is a good conductor. This ready availability of free electrons is also true of copper and most other metals.

Fig. 1-2B illustrates phosphorus with five valence electrons. When there are more than four valence electrons, they are tightly held in orbit so that normally none are free. Hence, phosphorus and similar elements are poor conductors (insulators).

Germanium (Fig. 1-2C) has four valence electrons. This makes it neither a good conductor nor a good insulator, hence its name "semiconductor." Silicon also has four valence electrons and is a semiconductor.

Germanium and silicon are remarkable in that their electrical conductivity can be radically increased by doping the extremely pure metal with tiny amounts of elements having one less or one more valence electron than they have. Aluminum, boron, gallium, and indium with three and phosphorus, arsenic, and antimony with five valence electrons are typical doping elements. Germanium and silicon are the base materials for semiconductors.

In a p-type of crystal (produced by adding small amounts of impurity such as aluminum) some of the atoms have one less electron than the other atoms, although the material is electrically neutral. The absence of an electron in the crystal structure can be considered as a "hole," and holes normally appear to flow in a direction opposite to the electron movement, carrying a positive charge.

In the n-type of crystal (made by adding an impurity such as phosphorus) there is an excess of electrons. Some of the atoms in the n-type crystals have more electrons than the regular atoms in the crystal material. In the n-type of material electrons move carrying a negative charge.

Diodes

A diode is formed by the combination of two types of semiconductor material, one p-type and one n-type. Under these conditions there is a limited flow of electrons from the n-type to the p-type, and a flow of holes from the p-type into the n-type. The n-type assumes a positive charge because of its loss of electrons, while the p-type assumes a negative charge because it has an excess of electrons (or a deficiency of positive holes). Thus the junction acts like an internal battery.

It is possible to connect an external battery to this junction so that it will either aid or oppose the internal battery. An external battery connected so that it aids the internal potential is said to forward bias the junction (Fig. 1-3A). Under these conditions of forward bias conduction takes place readily across the junction and electrons flow in the circuit.

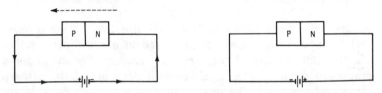

(A) Forward bias: Electrons flow.　(B) Reverse bias: No electrons flow.

Fig. 1-3. Bias methods.

If the external battery opposes the internal one, the junction is reverse biased (Fig. 1-3B). There will be no appreciable electron flow.

In the forward direction, the diode has a very low resistance; in the reverse direction, the diode has a very high resistance. The symbol for the semiconductor diode is an arrow (Fig. 1-4). Note that the direction the charged carriers (electrons and holes) flow

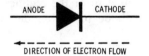

Fig. 1-4. The diode symbol.

is opposite to the arrowhead of the circuit symbol. As in a vacuum-tube diode, flow is from cathode to plate (anode).

Characteristics of one type of diode are shown in Fig. 1-5. When the junction is forward biased (positive anode or negative

11

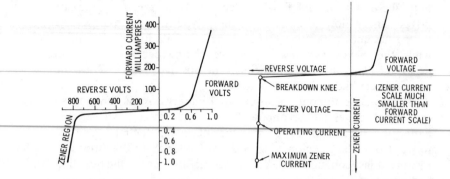

Fig. 1-5. Characteristic curve for
a silicon diode.

Fig. 1-6. Characteristic curve for
a zener diode.

cathode), the diode conducts. If a small negative voltage (reverse bias) is applied, the current is measured in microamperes rather than the milliamperes of the forward direction. The curve for a germanium diode is similar, although it does not show as sharp a front-to-back ratio. The diode still conducts much more in the forward direction than it does in the reverse direction.

When a sufficient reverse voltage (negative anode) is applied to a diode, it breaks down at a certain point (Fig. 1-6). This is the zener or breakdown voltage.

Breakdown in a silicon diode is not damaging to the device within limits, and the diode recovers when the reverse voltage is removed. The important feature is that, at breakdown, the voltage drop across it is almost independent of the amount of current. The diode can be used as a voltage regulator since its voltage drop is constant over a wide current range. The zener symbol is shown in Fig. 1-7: (A) is a single unit, and (B) is a symmetrical (double) unit.

The diode is the semiconductor equivalent of the rectifier tube. In both, electron flow is from the cathode to the anode, with a

(A) Single zener diode.

(B) Symmetrical zener diode.

Fig. 1-7. Zener diodes.

high resistance offered to flow in the reverse direction. The electron tube requires filament or heater power that the diode does not. The small size and longer life of the semiconductor are additional advantages in its favor. Where there are no special conditions or requirements, price is the determining factor as to which will be used.

The zener diode has an equivalent in the voltage-regulator tube. While the mechanics of their operation are quite different (one involves conduction in an ionized gas, the other conduction in a solid material), the net result is similar.

Transistors

A transistor consists of three layers of semiconductor material —a thin layer of one type with the other type on each side. There are two possible arrangements: n-type in the middle with p-type on each side (pnp) and just the opposite (npn). The center is called the base, one outside layer is called the emitter, and the other is known as the collector.

A voltage is applied to each junction for normal transistor operation. The emitter-base junction is forward biased (Fig. 1-8A) so that when switch E is closed, electrons and holes move to the junction, causing current in the emitter-base circuit. Bat-

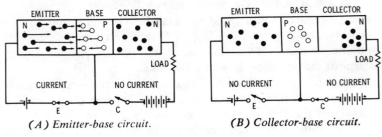

(A) Emitter-base circuit.   *(B) Collector-base circuit.*

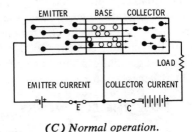

(C) Normal operation.

Fig. 1-8. Current in a transistor.

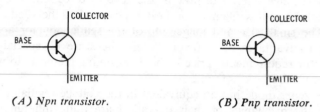

(A) Npn transistor.   (B) Pnp transistor.

Fig. 1-9. Transistor symbols.

tery voltage in this circuit is small. The base-collector junction is reverse biased (Fig. 1-8B); with switch C closed, the electrons and holes avoid the junction so there is no current in the collector-base circuit. Battery voltage in this circuit is large.

In Fig. 1-8C both switches E and C are now closed. Very few electrons flow in the emitter-base circuit; instead, practically all the electrons from the emitter go through the base (which in actual construction is very thin) into the reverse-biased collector. Once in the collector, they are propelled by the much higher collector voltage, completing their circuit through the load and back into the emitter terminal. The net result is voltage and power amplification from emitter circuit to collector circuit.

The action in Fig. 1-8 applies to npn transistors. To apply the same principles to pnp units, all polarities (batteries and charged carriers) would be reversed. Fig. 1-9 shows the symbols for npn and pnp transistors. Note that the normal flow of charged carriers is against the arrow of the emitter symbol.

Transistors are used in place of tubes in many cases. Compared to a tube, the transistor collector acts as the tube plate (anode), the base as the grid, and the emitter as the cathode.

In the tube, variation of grid voltage controls a larger voltage in the cathode-plate-load circuit, producing amplification. The tube triode is a voltage-operated device since the grid requires no current. In the transistor, variation in emitter-base current causes a larger current in the emitter-collector-load circuit to produce gain. The transistor is essentially a current-operated device since injection of current is necessary for opertaion.

HOW THE SCR WORKS

The SCR is made up of four layers of semiconductor material arranged pnpn. Its construction is shown in Fig. 1-10A. In function, the SCR has much in common with a diode, but the theory of its operation is best explained in terms of transistors.

Consider the SCR as a transistor pair, one pnp and the other npn, connected as in Fig. 1-10B and C. Electrode A (anode) is

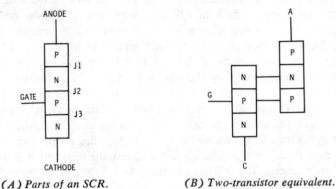

(A) Parts of an SCR.   *(B) Two-transistor equivalent.*

(C) Two-transistor schematic.

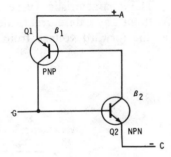

Courtesy Solid State Products, Inc.

Fig. 1-10. SCR structure.

attached to the upper p-layer, C (cathode) is part of the lower n-layer, and the (gate) terminal goes to the p-layer of the npn triode.

In operation the collector of Q2 drives the base of Q1, while the collector of Q1 feeds back to the base of Q2. Beta ß1 is the current gain of Q1, and ß2 is the current gain of Q2. The gain of this positive feedback loop is their product, ß1 times ß2. When the product is less than one, the circuit is stable; if the product is greater than unity, the circuit is regenerative. A small negative current applied to terminal G will bias the npn transistor into cutoff, and the loop gain is less than unity. Under these conditions,

15

the only current that can exist between output terminals C and A is the very small cutoff collector current of the two transistors. For this reason the impedance between A and C is very high.

When a positive current is applied to terminal G, transistor Q2 is biased into conduction, causing its collector current to rise. Since the current gain of Q2 increases with increased collector current, a point (called the breakdown point) is reached where the loop gain equals unity and the circuit becomes regenerative. Now, collector current of the two transistors rapidly increases to a value limited only by the external circuit. Both transistors are driven into saturation, and the impedance between A and C is very low. The positive current applied to terminal G, which served to trigger the self-regenerative action, is no longer required, since the collector of pnp transistor Q1 now supplies more than enough current to drive Q2. The circuit will remain on until it is turned off by reducing the collector current to a value below that necessary to maintain regeneration.

The characteristic curve for SCR's is shown in Fig. 1-11. Without any gate current, the leakage current remains very small as the forward voltage from cathode to anode is increased until

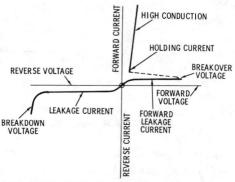

Fig. 1-11. Characteristic curve for an SCR.

the breakover point is reached. Here the center junction breaks down, the SCR fires, the drop across it becomes very low, and it conducts heavily.

The effect of a gate signal on the firing of an SCR is shown in Fig. 1-12. Breakdown of the center junction can be achieved at speeds approaching a microsecond by applying an appropriate signal to the gate lead, while holding the anode voltage constant.

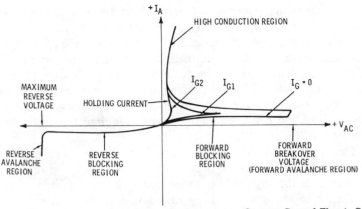

Courtesy General Electric Co.

Fig. 1-12. Characteristic curve for various gate signals.

After breakdown, the voltage across the device is so low that the current through it from cathode to anode is essentially determined by the load it is feeding.

In the operation of this device the important thing to remember is that a small current from gate to cathode can fire or trigger the SCR, changing it from practically an open circuit to a short circuit. The only way to change it back again (to commutate it) is to reduce the load current to a value less than the minimum holding current. Removing the gate current does nothing. Gate current is required only until the anode current has completely built up, about five millionths of a second (5 microseconds) in resistive-load circuits.

Until the SCR was developed, the thyratron was the only controlled rectifier available. Early SCR units were called solid-state thyratrons, and some were designed to plug into the thyratron socket. The thyratron is an electron tube, normally gas filled, that uses a filament or a heater. SCR's and thyratrons function in a very similar manner. Fig. 1-13 shows the schematic of each with

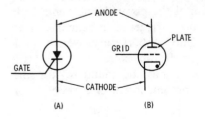

Fig. 1-13. Comparison of an SCR and a thyratron.

17

the corresponding elements labeled. In both types of devices control by the input signal is lost after they have been turned on. Once they are triggered, the control grid (thyratron) and the gate (SCR) have no further effect on the magnitude of the load current. To interrupt the load current, the load circuit must be opened by a switch, the plate (anode) voltage must be reduced below the ionizing potential of the gas (thyratron), or the forward current must be reduced below a minimum value required to sustain conduction (SCR).

The input resistance of the SCR is relatively low (approximately 100 ohms) and requires a current for triggering; the input resistance of the thyratron is exceptionally high, requiring a voltage input to the grid for triggering action.

The SCR is replacing the thyratron in a number of applications because of its many advantages. Warmup is eliminated with an SCR, because conduction starts at once. A thyratron can be damaged if a load is applied before the cathode heats up. To prevent accidental triggering during this period, relays, contactors, and other components with moving parts are sometimes added to the circuit. Such components can decrease the reliability of operation. Since there are no startup-voltage requirements for SCR's, power can be applied simultaneously to the gate and anode.

USING THE SCR

The basic action of an SCR is to switch power on very rapidly. All of the control circuits incorporating SCR's use this switching action in some form or other. In rectifier applications the SCR turns on only during the positive (or negative) half-cycles, thus providing pulsating direct current. Speed or power control is accomplished by switching the SCR on for longer or shorter periods of time. This switching can be performed at extremely high speeds (up to about 25 kc for some units). Only a very small amount of power is required to trigger it—under some circumstances, less than one-millionth of the power being controlled.

The SCR is a latching switch: once triggered, it remains on as long as current flows through it. Only a short pulse (less than 1 microsecond) is necessary to turn it on. Note that the SCR switches on only; some other means must be found to turn the switch off. Actually, this does not present much of a problem or restrict its use.

There are many ways of using the switching action of an SCR. One of the simplest is to turn on d-c power to any device when a sensing unit of some kind is activated. For example, a pressure switch could trigger an SCR, thus turning on an indicator showing excessive or insufficient pressure. A proximity detector could trigger an alarm through an SCR. Heat (or lack of heat) could be used to turn off (or on) valve controls. Almost anything capable of conversion to an electric pulse can be used to turn on power to any d-c operated device. The possibilities are limited only by the imagination of the designer.

Rectifying applications of the SCR are many. In fact, these are what give this semiconductor device its name. When alternating current is applied to a rectifier, only the positive (or negative)

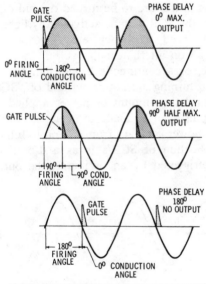

(SHADED AREAS REPRESENT ADJUSTABLE OUTPUT POWER)

Fig. 1-14. SCR control.

halves of the sine wave flow through. All of each positive half-cycle appears in the output. Using an SCR, however, the controlled rectifier may be turned on at any time during the half-cycle, thus controlling the amount of d-c power available, from the entire half-cycle to zero (Fig. 1-14). Since the output is actually d-c pulses, suitable filtering can be added if continuous direct current is needed. Thus any d-c operated device can have controlled amounts of power applied to it.

Notice that the SCR must be turned on at the desired time for each cycle. Circuitry for accomplishing this is discussed in Chapter 2.

When an a-c power source is used, turn-off of the SCR is accomplished automatically, since current and voltage drop to zero every half cycle. By using one SCR on positive alternations and one on negative, full-wave rectification can be accomplished; control is obtained over the entire sine wave. The SCR serves in this application just as its name implies—as a controlled rectifier of a-c voltage.

The SCR can be used as a static a-c switch. Its speed of operation and lack of moving parts give it many advantages where large amounts of power are to be turned on and off frequently. As in d-c operation, the SCR may be activated by light, heat, pressure, voltage, current, speed, frequency, etc. Two SCR's are required; they are triggered on alternate half cycles. The trigger can occur every half cycle, or a continuous trigger can be used.

In addition to turning a-c power on and off, SCR circuitry can be used to control the amount of power applied to an a-c load. The triggering pulse can be made to occur at any time during the cycle, so output power can vary from full on to full off (Fig. 1-15).

Another application of SCR's is as a d-c to a-c inverter. If two SCR's are triggered by an oscillator, the output is a square

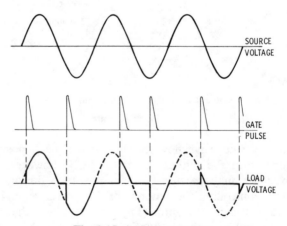

SOURCE VOLTAGE

GATE PULSE

LOAD VOLTAGE

Fig. 1-15. A-c power control.

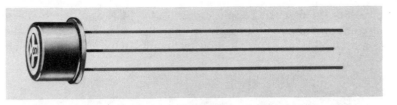

Courtesy Silicon Transistor Corp.

Fig. 1-16. A TO-5 case like that used for SCR's.

wave. This can be filtered into a sine wave, if it is desired. If a variable oscillator does the triggering, the frequency of the output will vary.

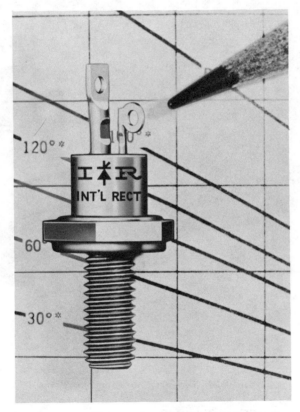

Courtesy International Rectifier Corp.

Fig. 1-17. A five-ampere SCR.

All of the preceding applications use the SCR as a switch. There are many variations of each so that the usefulness of SCR's is almost limitless. As production techniques improve and costs are

Courtesy International Rectifier Corp.
Fig. 1-18. Ten- and sixteen-ampere SCR's.

reduced, the SCR will appear in an increasing number of commercial applications.

TYPES OF SCR's

SCR's are manufactured by many companies who provide them in a variety of sizes and ratings. Some of the smallest units, capable of controlling up to 1.5 amps, are packaged in TO-5 cases, similar to those used for small-signal transistors (Fig. 1-16). All leads come out the bottom of the case, so it is very handy for mounting on printed-circuit boards.

A larger unit (Fig. 1-17) is capable of handling 5 amps of current. The stud is the anode, the long lead is the cathode, and

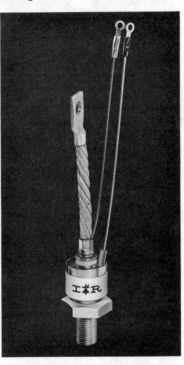

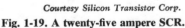

Courtesy Silicon Transistor Corp.
Fig. 1-19. A twenty-five ampere SCR.

Courtesy International Rectifier Corp.
Fig. 1-20. A seventy-ampere SCR.

the short lead is the gate. The schematic representation is printed on the case in a position such that it and the terminals correspond.

As the power-handling capacity of the SCR's increases, so does the unit size. Fig. 1-18 shows 16- and 20-amp SCR's, similar to the previous unit except for physical dimensions. A 25-amp SCR is shown in Fig. 1-19. Some units are designed to be press-fit into a heat sink so there is no stud, and the case is the anode under these circumstances. The long lead is the cathode, and the short one is the gate.

Larger units use flexible braided leads for the cathode, as shown in Fig. 1-20. This unit, which will switch 70 amps, has separate small-wire leads for connecting to the gate circuitry.

As improvements are made in manufacturing technology, the upper limits of SCR ratings are increased. At present, units are available that will control almost 500 amps of current with voltage ratings of over 1000 volts.

2

SCR Characteristics

The silicon controlled rectifier has three basic requirements when functioning as a power switch: a source of power, a load to be supplied with power, and a means (trigger circuitry) to turn the power on and off (Fig. 2-1). In mechanical switches such as the familiar light switch on the wall, there is little interaction between the triggering force and the power being switched. The effect of pushing the button or flipping the handle is the same no matter who or what does it.

Things are not quite so simple in SCR circuits: there are relationships and restrictions that must be observed between the power source, the load, and the triggering signal. This information is compiled and published by the manufacturers for each type of unit. A knowledge of what this information means is essential to the proper use of SCR's.

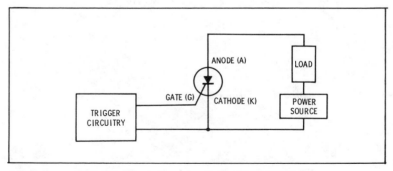

Fig. 2-1. Block diagram of a typical SCR circuit.

READING SPECIFICATIONS

There are limitations on the voltages and currents that can be applied to any given type of SCR; these are listed in the specifications found in SCR handbooks. Since units vary in power-handling capacity and price, it is desirable to select the one that meets the requirements of the application as closely as possible.

One complicating factor is that many parameters vary with temperature, so ratings must indicate the effect various temperatures have on operation. This is frequently done by graphs that look complicated. Unless one is designing for extremes of environment or maximum efficiency, it is usually possible to ignore temperatures other than 20°C or 25°C.

Terminology, and especially symbols, vary between manufacturers; it is not easy to recognize and compare data from different sources. The following are some of the principle terms and their symbols.

Forward Breakover Voltage

The voltage at which the SCR switches from a nonconducting to a conducting state without a triggering gate signal is the forward breakover voltage (Fig. 2-2). If a unit is to be used to switch a 400-volt source, one should be selected with a forward breakover voltage rating of more than 400 volts so that the unit will not switch on without being triggered. Symbols: BV_F, $V_{(BR)F}$, V_{BO}.

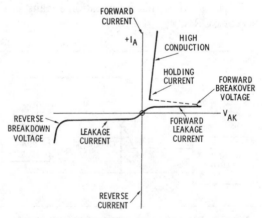

Fig. 2-2. Characteristic curve for an SCR.

Forward Blocking Voltage

The maximum voltage that can be applied across the SCR (anode to cathode) without the unit switching to a conducting state is called the forward blocking voltage. Some manufacturers list this rating in place of the forward breakover voltage since it deals with the same characteristics. A unit rated for 400 volts would be satisfactory for switching a 400-volt power supply. Symbols: V_{FOM}, $V_{F(OFF)}$, V_{FX}.

Forward Current Rating

The current capacity of an SCR is dependent on temperature, so current ratings are normally shown on graphs such as Fig. 2-3. The average forward current ($I_{F(AV)}$) that can be handled by an SCR is expressed in terms of the maximum temperature at which the SCR is expected to be operating. (The significance of the conduction angle is discussed in Chapter 4—Phase Control.)

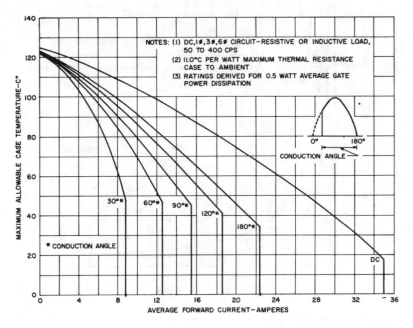

Courtesy General Electric Co.

Fig. 2-3. Typical average current specifications.

Also listed in the specifications is the RMS forward current (I_F), which is the average current that can be present without damaging the unit.

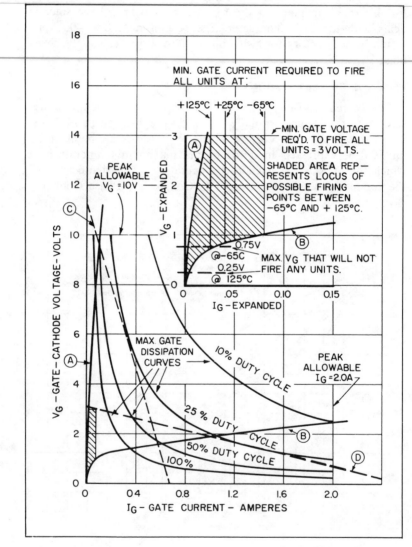

Courtesy General Electric Co.

Fig. 2-4. Typical gate trigger characteristics.

Gate Trigger Characteristics

The current and voltage applied to trigger an SCR into conduction are limited by the power that can be dissipated in the SCR without damage to the unit. This information is normally shown as a graph similar to Fig. 2-4, however, recommended values are sometimes shown in a table. Since there are variations between SCR's of the same type, the shaded area in the lower left-hand corner contains all the possible minimum trigger values for individual SCR's. The minimum values that are sure to trigger all units of a given type lie outside this shaded area. However, this area is bounded by three maximum limits. There is a maximum current, voltage, and power dissipation which cannot be exceeded without danger of permanent damage to the unit. Thus the preferred gate drive (firing circuit design criteria) is shown as an area in which any combination of voltage and current will create a satisfactory trigger. These characteristics, which are affected by temperature and the voltage and current being switched by the SCR, will be indicated on the specifications chart.

Other Ratings

The preceding ratings concern the power-handling and switching circuits of the SCR. Like all semiconductors, SCR's have many limitations that must be observed if they are to function properly for an indefinite period of time. Specification sheets for each type of each manufacturer show these limitations. Many concern the extremes caused by reversal of normal voltages. The reverse blocking voltage (V_{ROM} or V_R) is the maximum negative voltage which may be applied to the anode—the point at which reverse breakdown occurs (Fig. 2-2). Some units or circuit components can be damaged if this voltage is exceeded. Avalanche SCR's have been manufactured to offer protection at this point.

THE CHARACTERISTIC CURVE

The characteristic curve for SCR's (Fig. 2-2) provides a good picture of typical switching action. The voltage applied to the anode and cathode of the SCR (V_{AK}) is plotted on the horizontal axis. This is the voltage supplied by the power source of Fig. 2-1. On the vertical axis is the current through the SCR anode (I_A), which is also the current in the load circuit since the load is in series with the power supply and the SCR.

As the power-supply voltage increases from zero in a positive direction, there is a small leakage current which remains fairly constant for a wide range of voltages. In other words, the SCR is turned off. This slight leakage current can be disregarded in most applications. When the power-supply voltage (V_{AK}) reaches the forward breakdown voltage, the SCR begins to conduct, and the voltage across the SCR drops. Full conduction is reached rapidly. Most of the power-supply voltage appears across the load; the drop across the SCR is so small as to be disregarded in most cases. The current in the SCR is limited only by the resistance of the load. The SCR acts as a closed switch, allowing power to flow through the load circuit. It will continue to flow as long as the holding current for the SCR is maintained. The forward breakover voltage is the critical factor here in turning the SCR on.

From Fig. 2-5 it is apparent that the current in the gate circuit of the SCR (I_G) affects the forward breakover voltage. Three different values are plotted: I_G equals zero; I_G equals I_{GT} (the current required to fire the SCR when a small voltage is applied

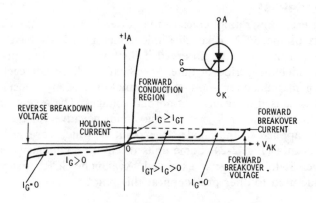

Fig. 2-5. Characteristic curve showing variations in gate current.

to the anode); and a value of I_G between zero and I_{GT}. Note that the forward breakover voltage drops as the gate current increases, and the former has a maximum value when there is no gate current.

This suggests several possibilities that can be used to fire the SCR:

1. It will fire when V_{AK} is sufficiently large even without a triggering gate current.
2. If V_{AK} is held constant, introducing gate current of appropriate magnitude will fire the SCR.
3. If I_G is held constant, the SCR will fire when V_{AK} reaches a certain value.

The SCR is called a latching switch because gate current can be used only to fire the SCR. Once it is conducting, the SCR cannot be turned off by any action in the trigger circuitry. To open the load circuit, current through the load (and the SCR) must be reduced below the holding current, as shown in Fig. 2-5. Techniques for doing this are discussed under "Turn-Off Methods" later in this chapter.

TURN-ON METHODS

The SCR may be triggered into conduction (turned on) by several methods. A-c signals, varying direct current, and pulses are all used in numerous applications.

D-C Gate Bias

Direct current can be used in several ways to trigger an SCR into conduction. One possible circuit is shown in Fig. 2-6. When a fixed d-c voltage is applied to the SCR from the power source so that the anode is positive and the cathode is negative, a definite

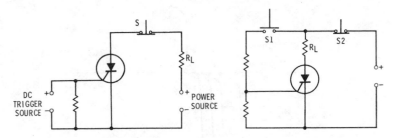

Fig. 2-6. D-c turn-on with   Fig. 2-7. D-c turn-on with derived
independent trigger source.   trigger source.

value of gate current (I_{GT}) is required to fire (turn-on) the SCR. The polarity must be such that the gate is positive with respect to the cathode. The turn-on sequence is as follows:

As long as the gate current is less than I_{GT}, the SCR will not turn on. When it increases to I_{GT}, the SCR turns on, allowing power to flow to the load. Even though the trigger source is reduced, the SCR will remain in its conducting state. However, depressing push-button switch S momentarily after the triggering signal has been removed, turns the SCR off, and it will stay off until the next time it is triggered. This is the solid-state equivalent of a latching switch.

A possible application of this circuit might be in a security alarm system. The d-c trigger source could be a battery and switch arrangement on a door so that opening the door could close a switch and apply a d-c voltage to the SCR gate. The load could be a d-c powered burglar alarm. If the door were opened, the SCR would be triggered, and the burglar alarm would be turned on. It would continue to sound even after the door was closed, since it could only be turned off by depressing pushbutton S.

Fig. 2-7 shows how the d-c bias can be obtained from a voltage-divider network across the voltage source. The resulting action is similar to Fig. 2-6.

Under normal circumstances d-c gate bias should not be used for triggering when the power source for the load is alternating current. During the reverse part of the a-c cycle, the reverse current from anode to cathode of the SCR would be greatly increased by an appreciable flow of positive gate current. The com-

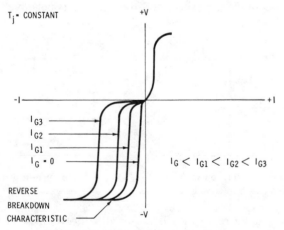

Fig. 2-8. Reverse breakdown as affected by trigger current.

bination could exceed the ratings of the SCR and destroy it. Fig. 2-8 illustrates how the reverse breakdown characteristic is affected by the gate current (I_G).

A-C Gate Signal

An a-c gate signal can be used to turn on the SCR (Fig. 2-9). The gate current required is determined mainly by the load source

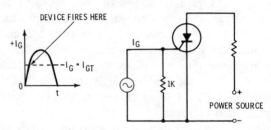

Fig. 2-9. A-c turn-on.

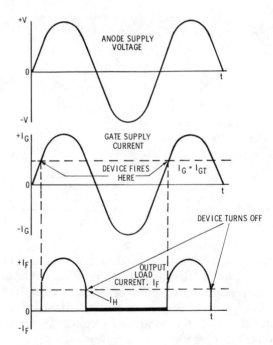

Fig. 2-10. Curves for a-c source and trigger.

voltage; since the trigger needs to exist for only a very short time (less than 5 microseconds), alternating current may be substituted for direct current. When the a-c gate current reaches I_{GT}, the SCR fires. No mechanism for turn-off is shown here, though a practical circuit would contain one. The d-c supply keeps the SCR on even after the gate current drops below I_{GT}.

An a-c gate signal may be used when an a-c power source is used (Fig. 2-9). Fig. 2-10 shows the relationships between the SCR anode voltage, the gate current, and the output load current. Here the gate current is shown in phase with the anode supply voltage. When the gate current increases to I_{GT}, the controlled rectifier is triggered on. It remains in the on condition until the current through the load and the SCR drops below the holding current I_H (Fig. 2-5). Holding current is always a small fraction of the normal load current.

The controlled rectifier can be made to fire at any point in the forward-biased portion of the cycle by changing the phase of the

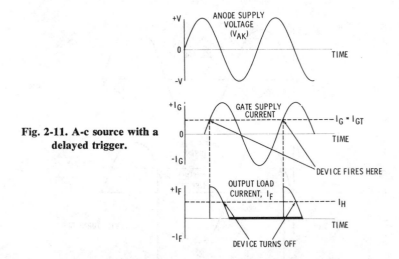

Fig. 2-11. A-c source with a delayed trigger.

gate current in relation to that of the anode voltage. (Fig. 2-11). When I_G is displaced from its normal in-phase position, there will be trigger current during a portion of the time when the SCR anode is negative. To prevent damage to the SCR it is desirable to place a diode in series with the controlled rectifier, shown in Fig. 2-12 as the reverse blocking diode. This prevents the negative half-cycles of the power supply from reaching the anode of the SCR.

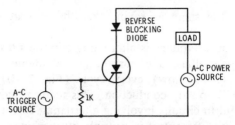

Fig. 2-12. Use of a blocking diode.

Pulse Triggers for the Gate

From the manner in which an a-c signal is used as a gate trigger, it is apparent that only parts of the sine wave are needed. As long as the required amounts of voltage and current are supplied to the SCR gate for a short period of time (less than a microsecond) the source or shape of the trigger does not matter. Pulses may be derived from the power source supplying the load. Where circuitry is provided to change the phase of the power source, the power applied to the load can be varied over a wide range.

Triggering pulses can be derived from a source independent of the power supply. Multivibrator or oscillator circuits can be used to furnish a trigger that can be varied over a wide range of frequencies. Pulses in a computer circuit may provide the gate signal to trigger an SCR.

Part of the usefulness of the SCR is due to the small amount of power required to trigger it into conduction and the variety of ways this trigger can be obtained. Further details on trigger circuitry are given in Chapter 3.

TURN-OFF METHODS

The SCR resembles a latching switch in that its basic function is to turn on current or power to a load when a signal is applied, and then to maintain the closed circuit when the signal is removed. Turning off the power must be accomplished through separate circuitry.

To stop an SCR from conducting, the cathode-to-anode current (which is also the load current) must be reduced to a value lower than the holding current. For most SCR's the latter is 5 to 20 milliamperes. Since normal load current is in the ampere region, this is almost the same as saying that the current must be reduced to zero.

Where the source voltage is alternating current, turn-off is automatic. The a-c voltage and current at the anode of the SCR drop to zero (and below) every cycle (Fig. 2-10), effectively causing the SCR to stop conduction. This feature makes the SCR extremely useful in circuits involving alternating current. Complete turn-on and turn-off control is possible by working with the gate signals only. SCR's are available that will handle a-c frequencies up to 25 kc.

Where d-c power is being switched, turn-off arrangements vary from simple switches to self-timing circuitry.

Switch Turn-Off

Probably the most obvious way to accomplish turn-off is with a switch, and this can be very practical in some SCR circuits. Fig. 2-13 shows two possible variations.

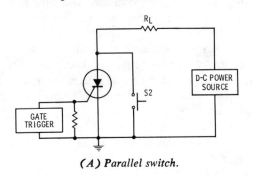

(A) Parallel switch.

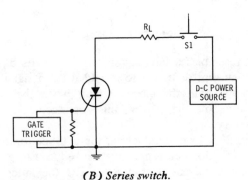

(B) Series switch.

Fig. 2-13. Turn-off using a switch.

A normally open pushbuttton switch is used in Fig. 2-13A. When the switch is closed, the anode and cathode of the SCR are shorted together, reducing the voltage (and current) across them to zero. Power will still flow to the load however, since there is a complete circuit from source to load. Releasing the switch puts the SCR (which has been cut off) back in the circuit. Power through the load is now interrupted since the SCR is nonconducting.

In Fig. 2-13B a normally closed pushbutton accomplishes the same objective. Depressing the switch opens the load circuit, thus reducing the SCR current to zero. When the pushbutton is released the circuit is reset; the next time the SCR is triggered, power will be applied to the load.

Capacitor Turn-Off

In controlling d-c power one can use circuit components for the turn-off instead of depending on a manual switch. Either a series capacitor or a shunt capacitor may be employed. As one method, Fig. 2-14A shows a series-capacitor or hammer circuit. When the SCR is triggered, capacitor C charges to approximately twice the d-c supply voltage by the inductive action of L. The discharging capacitor reverse biases the SCR, turning it off. In this circuit current is delivered to the load in pulses, one pulse for each trigger signal. The length of the pulses is determined by the values of capacitance and inductance.

Fig. 2-14B shows a simple circuit with a capacitor in series with a controlled rectifier. This circuit can be used as a final stage in turn-off circuitry since it turns itself off. When capacitor C approaches full charge, the current is reduced below the holding current value, and the SCR is turned off.

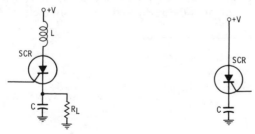

(A) Capacitor and inductor.   (B) Capacitor only.

Fig. 2-14. Series capacitor turn-off.

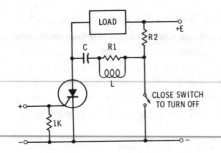

Fig. 2-15. Shunt switch turn-off.

The circuit in Fig. 2-15 combines a capacitor and a manual switch to provide turn-off action. This has the advantage over the simple switch of Fig. 2-13 in that the full load current does not pass through the switch. With the SCR in its conducting state, capacitor C charges up to the d-c source minus the voltage drop across the SCR. The time required to charge capacitor C is determined by R2. When the switch is closed, capacitor C will produce a back bias for the SCR, allowing the SCR to regain its forward blocking ability. Capacitor C also supplies the load current for a short interval. The R-L network in series with capacitor C is used to limit the reverse recovery current.

The value of C depends upon the load impedance and the recovery time of the controlled rectifier. C is also dependent upon the amount of peak reverse recovery current allowed to flow through the device during the time that it is reverse biased. These will vary with the individual circuits and the SCR that is used.

Capacitor-SCR Turn-Off

The switch in Fig. 2-15 used to turn off the SCR can be replaced with another controlled rectifier in some applications. This circuit (Fig. 2-16) is quite similar to a latching relay with two inputs, one to latch the relay and one to unlatch it. SCR1 can

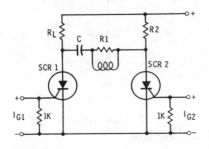

Fig. 2-16. Two-SCR turn-off.

be turned off by turning SCR2 on; SCR2 can be turned off by turning SCR1 on. The resulting current in the load is a series of pulses as the two gates are alternately triggered. In this circuit one must be sure that both inputs are never energized at the same time. The first SCR is chosen to carry the required current for the load, while the second SCR may be one with a much lower rating. This circuit can be made with two equal SCR's for applications where two separate loads are to be handled.

Turn-off of the SCR's is accomplished by the discharging of capacitor C. When SCR1 is fired, capacitor C charges up through resistor R to the positive supply (less the drop across SCR1) with the polarity shown. When SCR2 is fired, the capacitor discharges, placing a negative voltage on the anode of SCR1 and thus turning it off. Capacitor C then charges up through R_L and SCR2 to a polarity opposite that shown. When SCR1 is again fired, SCR2 is turned off by the same process as above. The proper value for capacitor C is determine by the load current, the applied d-c voltage, and the turn-off time of the SCR.

3

Static Switching

The two states of an SCR, conducting and nonconducting, correspond exactly to the on and off positions of a conventional electric switch. SCR's are finding wide applications in circuits where they perform static switching; i.e., they turn a signal or power on or off. (Static switching is contrasted with controlled switching of SCR's where the amount of power applied to a load is regulated by varying the duty cycle—relative proportion of on and off time—of the SCR.)

Static switching using the SCR has advantages over other static switching techniques. These include:

1. No contact bounce.
2. Less mechanical noise.
3. Less radio-frequency interference.
4. Low maintenance since there are no moving parts to wear.
5. No arcing (necessary for explosive atmospheres).
6. Not affected by shocks or vibration.
7. Can be mounted in any orientation.
8. High switching speed.
9. Small size in many applications.
10. Adaptable to special space factors.
11. Lowest cost in many applications.
12. High power gain.

There are some limitations to using SCR's. Sometimes the 0.5- to 1.0-volt drop between the cathode and the anode in the conducting state cannot be tolerated in a circuit. In mechanical switches there is practically no voltage drop across the contacts.

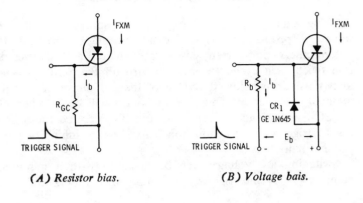

(A) Resistor bias.   (B) Voltage bais.

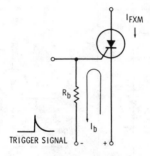

(C) Current bias.

Fig. 3-1. Gate biasing methods.

SCR circuits become very complex for multiple-pole switches where several switches must be handled simultaneously. Isolation between signal and power circuits is difficult in many applications.

The SCR is very useful for high-gain switching directly from low-level control signals. Usually the SCR eliminates the need for intermediate stages of amplification of the triggering signal. Even a small signal can turn on or off very large power sources; gains of a million are not unusual.

Where high sensitivity is not required, any degree of reduced sensitivity can be achieved by gate biasing. This can be accomplished in two ways: by connecting a resistor of suitable size between the gate and cathode terminals of the SCR (Fig. 3-1A), or by returning the gate resistor to a negative voltage source (Fig. 3-1B). Since biasing reduces firing sensitivity, the correct resistance value is important in the circuit design.

SWITCHING A-C VOLTAGES

Using alternating current for a power source in SCR circuits solves one problem quickly and easily: turning off the SCR. By its nature, alternating current passes through zero and reverses direction twice each cycle. In order to turn off the SCR, the current in it must drop below the value of the holding current that will maintain conduction. Thus, an a-c source will be switched off by the SCR at the end of each positive half-cycle, and the SCR cannot be triggered into conduction before the beginning of the next positive half-cycle.

Switching a-c voltages can be achieved with a minimum of components by means of the circuits shown in Fig. 3-2. In Fig.

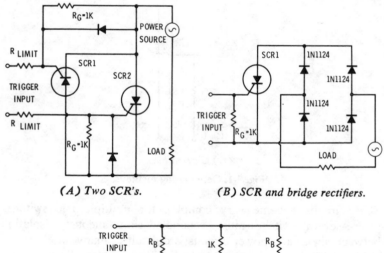

(A) Two SCR's.   *(B) SCR and bridge rectifiers.*

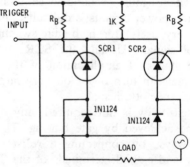

(C) Two SCR's in a bridge circuit.

Fig. 3-2. Switching a-c power.

3-2A the first half of the a-c signal is handled by SCR1, then the second half is switched by SCR2 when the a-c polarity reverses. Thus a single trigger signal to the gates of both SCR's will turn on the full a-c power. The advantages of this system are simplicity and high efficiency due to a low forward voltage drop.

The power to the load can be switched with a single SCR, using a bridge circuit of four diodes (Fig. 3-2B). This uses only one SCR, even though both positive and negative half-cycles of the power supply are applied to the load. For the same load current the SCR in Fig. 3-2B must handle twice as much current (and be rated twice as high) as each SCR in Fig. 3-2A. Two of the rectifiers in the bridge may be replaced with SCR's (Fig. 3-2C).

Note that several types of triggers can be used in these three circuits. In Figs. 3-2A and B, sensors with a d-c output, such as photocells, thermocouples, and piezoelectric crystals could be used as trigger sources to switch a wide variety of a-c operated devices. If direct current is used, one SCR will be turned on at the beginning of each half-cycle of the power source, and full a-c power will be applied to the load. When the d-c trigger is removed, the SCR's will stop conducting on the next half-cycle.

An a-c trigger can also be used in these circuits. Probably the simplest would be one derived from the power source, since the trigger needs to come at the beginning of each half-cycle of the power supply. The a-c trigger would have to be twice the source frequency for Figs. 3-2B and C, since a positive trigger is needed at the beginning of each half-cycle.

Note that SCR's do not latch on for an indefinite period of time when an a-c power source is used. Actually, they conduct only until the end of each half-cycle when they must again be triggered. If a d-c signal is used as a trigger, the SCR will fire on each positive alternation of the power supply. However, when the trigger is interrupted, the SCR conducts only until the end of that half-cycle, so turn-off occurs very quickly.

The single SCR in Fig. 3-3 acts as a half-wave rectifier when used with an a-c voltage source. It will block both the positive and the negative half-cycles until a positive control signal is applied to the gate. When this occurs, the SCR will conduct during the positive half-cycle and block during the negative half-cycle for as long as the control signal is present. When the control signal is removed, the SCR will block both half-cycles again, since it automatically turns off at the end of each positive half-cycle.

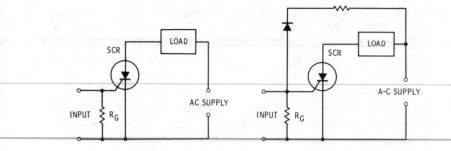

Fig. 3-3. Simple half-wave a-c switch.

Fig. 3-4. A-c switching with diode protection.

The circuit in Fig. 3-3 acts as a simple a-c static switch that supplies rectified half-wave direct current to the load. The input control signal can be alternating current, direct current, or pulses. If the load is inductive, a diode placed across it (called a freewheeling diode) results in a continuous current through the load during the negative half-cycle. The inductive field built up during the positive half-cycle returns stored energy during the negative alternation. The diode polarity permits this current flow in the same direction as during the positive alternation.

When an a-c power source is used, the positive control voltage applied to the SCR gate must be kept at a low value during the negative half-cycle of the power source because of reverse leakage current. This current increases as the positive gate current increases, and, if leakage current becomes large enough, it can

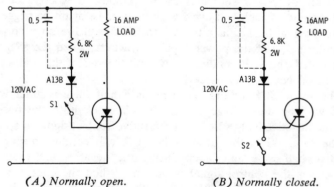

(A) Normally open.   *(B) Normally closed.*
Fig. 3-5. Manual switch for firing SCR's.

cause thermal runaway. The reverse half-cycle leakage current amounts to about one half of the positive gate current. By using a series resistance and diode as in Fig. 3-4, a bucking current can be obtained which will cancel the effect of any current flow in the other direction during the negative half-cycle.

Fig. 3-5 shows circuit details for heater loads, contactor drivers, limit switches, and other applications where half-wave a-c power must be switched. The top end of 6.8K resistor can also be connected to the other side of the load (the anode of the SCR) for minimum gate losses when the SCR is energized.

In Fig. 3-5A the closing of the switch fires the SCR through the load; in Fig. 3-5B the opening of the switch fires the SCR. If S1 and S2 are manually operated switches, they will need to handle only a few milliamperes of current to switch 16 amperes.

SWITCHING D-C VOLTAGES

When the source voltage is direct current, the SCR becomes a latching relay—once it is triggered, conduction continues indefinitely. A second action is necessary to cut off the SCR unless the circuit is set up to cut off after a definite period of time.

There are two choices of turn-off methods. The first is to interrupt the current in the load circuit, which is normally accomplished by opening a switch. While this has many possible applications, it is limited because the full load current must be switched.

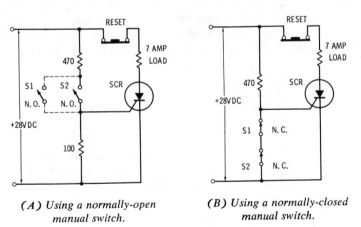

(A) Using a normally-open
manual switch.

(B) Using a normally-closed
manual switch.

Fig. 3-6. Switching direct current with SCR's.

45

SCR's are capable of handling much larger currents than it is practical to turn off with a mechanical switch.

Another method of turning off an SCR is to use forced commutation. Here power from some other sources (normally a capacitor) is switched into the load circuit in such a manner as to oppose the normal flow and reduce the SCR current to zero.

Fig. 3-6 shows two possible circuits for d-c static switching. These are practical arrangements for replacing electromechanical latching relays. Once they are turned on by a control signal, they will remain on indefinitely. To turn them off, the anode current is reduced below the dropout level by depressing the Reset button. Fig. 3-6A shows a simple latching-switch circuit. If S1 or S2 is closed for a moment, the positive drop across the 100 ohms triggers the SCR on. By way of contrast, Fig. 3-6B requires a momentary opening of a switch to trigger the SCR. In either case 12 microwatts input power (.6 volts at 20 microamperes) for a time duration of 1 microsecond or longer will turn on load power of 200 watts or more, depending on the SCR.

The SCR will remain latched at any load current above the dropout level, which is very low. It will work as well with small loads (10 ma) as it does at higher load currents.

The circuit can be used as a single-contact latching switch for direct control of a given load. It is useful for driving relay coils or similar electromagnetic loads. A conventional d-c relay can be converted to a high-sensitivity latching relay using an SCR. For inductive loads, a diode may be necessary across the load to eliminate voltage surge when the power is removed.

SCR's handling d-c power may also be turned off (commutated) by switching current from some energy source into the circuit in

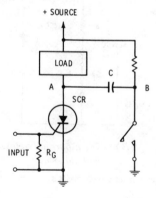

Fig. 3-7. D-c switching with
shunt-capacitor turn-off.

such a way that it opposes the original current, reducing it to zero. This is usually accomplished by charging a capacitor and then discharging it into the circuit.

A shunt capacitor is used in Fig. 3-7 to turn off the SCR. The operation of the circuit is as follows. The SCR is off until a triggering signal is applied to the input in order to turn it on. When the SCR is conducting, the voltage at point A is approximately $+1V$. Capacitor C charges through the series resistance until point B reaches the full positive supply voltage. Even after the triggering signal is removed, power flows to the load. When switch S is closed, point B is at ground potential, and the charge on the capacitor makes point A negative with respect to ground. The capacitor discharges into the load, reducing the current to zero. With no holding current in the SCR, it ceases to conduct.

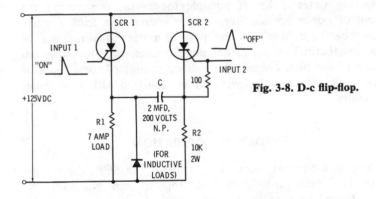

Fig. 3-8. D-c flip-flop.

If another SCR is used in place of switch S, turn-off can be accomplished electronically, as shown in Fig. 3-8. Operation is identical to that described above, except that turn-off is accomplished by a momentary low-level positive pulse at input 2. This circuit is actually a power flip-flop. When SCR1 is turned on, SCR2 is turned off by the charge on capacitor C. When SCR2 is turned on, SCR1 is turned off by C. A second load can take the place of R2 so that switching between two loads R1 and R2 is easily accomplished. This circuit is the solid-state equivalent of the SPDT (single-pole double-throw) mechanical contact arrangement.

4

Phase Control

The ability of SCR's to switch rapidly from nonconducting to conducting states makes it possible to control (i.e., vary) the amount of power applied from an a-c source to a load. Control circuitry can be used to vary the speed of motors, the brightness of lights, the thermal output of heating elements, etc. By taking advantage of the high current and voltage ratings of some types of SCR's, large amounts of power can be regulated with a minimum of circuitry.

THEORY OF OPERATION

When an a-c power source is switched by an SCR, the current is turned off each time the current drops to zero. Normally, the SCR is turned on by a trigger pulse at the beginning of each a-c cycle, and maximum power flows to the load. Under these conditions the trigger is said to be "in phase" with the source voltage. This is a conduction angle (α) of 180° or a firing angle of 0°.

Fig. 4-1A is a graphic presentation of this situation. On the upper graph is shown the triggering signal, which consists of a series of short pulses. The exact nature of the trigger is not very critical, except there are minimum and maximum voltages and currents specified for each type of SCR. The lower graph shows the actions in the load circuit. Note that the time axis is the same for both graphs. The dotted sine wave is the source voltage as applied to the anode of the SCR, and the shaded area is a measure of the power flowing through the SCR to the load. The firing

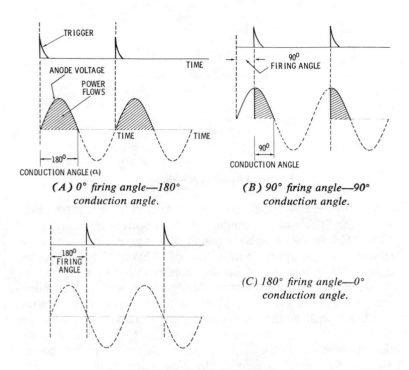

(A) 0° firing angle—180° conduction angle.

(B) 90° firing angle—90° conduction angle.

(C) 180° firing angle—0° conduction angle.

Fig. 4-1. Triggering an SCR.

angle is the number of degrees the voltage sine wave has gone through before the trigger pulse occurs—in this case 0°. The conduction angle (α) represents the actual time the SCR is tuned on. Since conduction occurs in an SCR only when the anode is positive, power from an a-c source can flow half the time.

If a means could be found to delay the trigger pulse, then the SCR would be turned on later (but would be turned off at the same time). Power would be applied to the load a shorter period of time, so the average power would be less. Varying the trigger over a firing angle from 0° to 180° would control the power applied from maximum to zero.

Phase control does exactly this. The phase of the trigger pulse is delayed in reference to the applied source voltage, so the time the SCR conducts varies. The result is that the power to the load is controlled.

In Fig. 4-1B a firing angle of 90° is shown. Under these circumstances only half the power will be applied to the load, as

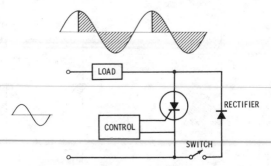

Fig. 4-2. Phase control—half-wave.

compared to Fig. 4-1A. If the firing angle is 180° or greater (Fig. 4-1C), the SCR will not conduct, and no power will flow.

The SCR in the previous example actually rectifies since only positive voltages appear across the load. Even at a conduction angle of 180°, only half of the available power is switched to the load. Fig. 4-2 shows a circuit where the power is controlled through the entire sine wave. If the switch is closed, power varies from full to half as the conduction angle decreases from 180° to 0°. This is because the rectifier passes half of the sine wave normally blocked by the SCR. When the switch is opened, power will vary from half to zero as the conduction angle is changed from 180° to 0°.

The full wave is controlled by two SCR's in the circuit of Fig. 4-3. Note that the trigger must be of the same polarity as the source voltage—positive during the first half-cycle and negative during the second—in order to trigger the SCR's at the proper

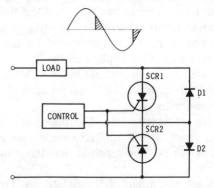

Fig. 4-3. Phase control—full wave.

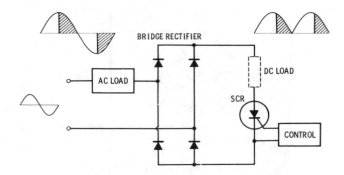

Fig. 4-4. Phase control—full wave with bridge rectifier.

time. This circuit gives smoother control over the full range than the previous one.

The load in Fig. 4-4 may be either a-c or d-c operated, and a single SCR is used to control the power. By phase-shifting the trigger pulse, power to the load—either a-c or d-c—can be varied continuously from zero to maximum. The location of the load in the circuit, in series with the source or the SCR, determines whether a-c or d-c power is applied to it.

TRIGGER CIRCUITS

In order to trigger an SCR in a phase-control circuit, three things are required. First, the trigger must have the proper magnitude of current and voltage to turn on the SCR. This becomes pretty much of a design problem to select the proper circuit components based on the requirements of the particular type of SCR being used. Second, the trigger must be capable of being varied through the desired phase and time relationships. The firing angle between the power source and the trigger has to be capable of smooth variation if phase control is to be successful. Third, the trigger circuitry must be able to translate the information from a sensor unit that is measuring heat, light, pressure, speed, etc., into trigger pulses that vary in their time relationship to the power source.

In order to relate to the power source, most trigger circuits derive their power from it. The circuitry then involves shaping the pulse and placing it at the proper point of time. There are many different arrangements to accomplish this.

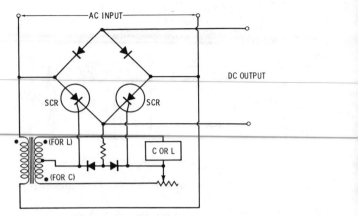

Fig. 4-5. Phase shift control—d-c output.

Phase Shift

In the phase-shift method of firing the SCR, an R-C or R-L network is used to delay the gate signal with respect to the anode voltage. Many variations of phase-shift networks that have been used to fire thyratrons have been adapted and modified from thyratron to SCR operation. They offer a simple method of timing the SCR gate pulse in reference to a-c power-line variations.

Fig. 4-5 illustrates a basic SCR phase-shift network for full-wave phase control with a d-c output to a load. To utilize both halves of the a-c cycle, the SCR's are connected in a bridge circuit and are fired by gate pulses on alternate half-cycles.

Note that this circuit can shift the firing angle 180°, giving almost complete control of the a-c power supply. If an inductor is used instead of a capacitor for the phase-shifting element, connections to the secondary of the transformer must be reversed, because inductors have just the opposite effect from capacitors in shifting phase.

The SCR trigger in this circuit is a sine wave, the same frequency as the power supply. When the current reaches the value necessary to trigger the SCR, the latter fires and continues to conduct until the anode voltage drops to zero. A manually operated potentiometer is shown as the point of control in this circuit.

The simple circuit in Fig. 4-6 is very similar to Fig. 4-5, except it provides half-wave rectified alternating current to the load. An

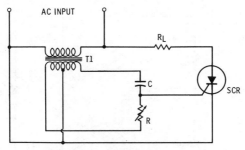

Fig. 4-6. Phase shift control—half-wave a-c output.

R-C phase-shift network, consisting of a fixed capacitor and a variable resistor, is connected so as to supply the gate drive requirements of the SCR. Turning the potentiometer varies the phase angle between the a-c input and the gate signal, so the SCR is triggered at varying points in the a-c cycle. As in the previous circuit, the triggering signal is a sine wave.

An inductor can be substituted for the fixed capacitor to provide the phase shift. When this is done, the connections to the transformer secondary must be reversed.

Neon Pulse Trigger

Firing an SCR with a sine-wave trigger has disadvantages, particularly in full-wave circuits where two SCR's are involved. The normal variation in units may result in them firing at different voltages and consequently at different times, since the sine wave rises at a relatively slow rate (Fig. 4-7A). If SCR1 fires at 3 volts and SCR2 fires at 5 volts, there can be a difference of several milliseconds in their firing time.

A much more satisfactory trigger is a rapidly rising pulse, such as Fig. 4-7B. Here, the rise time can easily be less than a micro-

(A) Sine wave.   *(B) Pulse.*

Fig. 4-7. Trigger waveforms.

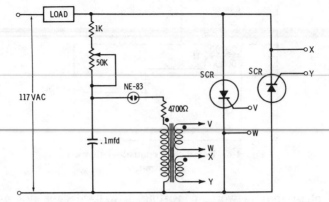

Fig. 4-8. Neon trigger circuit.

second so that for practical purposes all SCR's of the same type would be triggered at the same time, or at the same point in the power-supply cycle, giving a symmetrical output.

One of the many variations of pulse triggers for the firing of silicon controlled rectifiers is shown in Fig. 4-8. The 1K resistor and

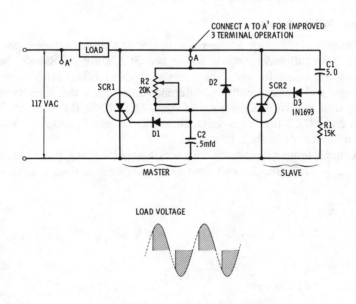

Fig. 4-9. Capacitor trigger circuit.

50K potentiometer are in series with the 0.1-mfd capacitor across the 117-volt line. When the capacitor reaches a sufficiently high voltage, the neon lamp fires, producing a sharp pulse twice each cycle through the transformer primary.

The transformer windings are arranged so that a positive pulse appears on one gate the first half-cycle and on the other gate the next half-cycle. The resulting conduction of the SCR's provides full-wave a-c power to the load. As the resistance of the potentiometer is lowered, the charging time for the capacitor is lessened. This produces pulses earlier in the a-c cycle, increasing the power applied to the load.

Capacitor Triggering

Fig. 4-9 uses the charging time of a capacitor to determine when the SCR gate is triggered. Although the control potentiometer is in the master circuitry, the slave section reflects its action, varying the firing time of SCR2. At the start of the first cycle, C2 charges at a rate determined by the setting of potentiometer R2. At the same time C1 starts to charge at a slower rate since the time constant of the C1-R1 combination is much greater. When C2 becomes sufficiently charged to trigger the gate of SCR1, the latter fires, reducing the voltage across it (and C1-R1) to practically zero. C1 now starts to discharge. By now the phase of the a-c source voltage has reversed, and the anode of SCR2 is becoming positive. However, C1 must be completely discharged and re-

Courtesy Acromag, Inc.

Fig. 4-10. Magnetic amplifier using a saturable reactor.

charged in the opposite direction before SCR2 will fire. The longer the time that SCR1 conducts, the more C1 discharges, the sooner SCR2 fires, and vice versa. Thus SCR2 follows the pattern of conduction set by SCR1, and the output is symmetrical.

MAGNETIC TRIGGERS

The use of magnetic triggers for thyratron circuits is quite wide spread. It is natural, then, that they should be carried over into the operation of semiconductor-controlled circuitry. The basic component of magnetic circuitry is the saturable reactor, a transformer that is designed so that the current through the coils is capable of creating a larger magnetic flux than the core can handle. A typical small saturable reactor can be seen in Fig. 4-10.

Saturable Reactors

A simple saturable reactor in series with an a-c source and a load is shown in Fig. 4-11. Waveforms across the various parts of the circuit are included. When a-c voltage is applied, the magnetic flux builds up from time T_0 until T_1, the core saturation point. During this time period there is a large voltage drop across the reactor, as shown, but very little, if any, drop across the load be-

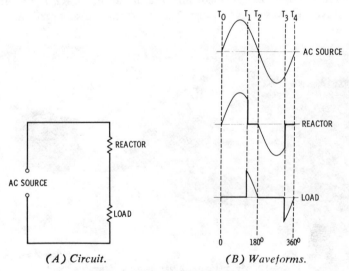

(A) Circuit.   (B) Waveforms.

Fig. 4-11. Saturable reactor.

cause the reactor impedance is very high as compared to the load resistance.

But at the T_1 time, the reactor saturates—it can support no further flux change—and its voltage drops to zero. This is just like passing a bar magnet through a coil of wire. As long as the bar moves through the coil, there will be a current in the coil and a voltage drop across it. But as soon as you stop moving the bar magnet through the coil, the current ceases. In the same manner, when saturation is reached at T_1, there is an abrupt change in the circuit. Because the reactor impedance drops to a low value, there is a voltage drop across the load. Now the load resistance is the only effective impedance to current flow; hence, it has the voltage drop as shown.

The time from T_1 to T_2 is the conduction angle for an output. The same thing occurs on the negative alternation where the conduction angle is from T_3 to T_4. This sharp pulse-like output can be used, for example, to fire a thyratron or an SCR that may be controlling the rotation of a motor. By varying the reactor output, it is thus possible to control the motor speed.

The simple reactor in the previous figure lacks a means of control which is required for actual use. A system such as that in Fig. 4-12 is required where an easily varied current can control the power applied to a load. Direct current, adjustable by R1, varies the magnetic flux and consequently the output winding impedance. If R2 is a set of lights, such as used in theatre, and R1 is the light control, a simple industrial application may be seen. Turning R1 will dim or brighten the footlights or houselights as required.

Operation of the reactor depends on these two windings and their inter-relationship. The basic fact of operation is this: when

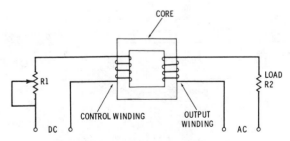

Fig. 4-12. Controlling a saturable reactor.

saturation is reached, no increase in current flow can change the magnetic field. Because the current in the control winding changes the amount of flux and hence the degree of magnetization, the load coil impedance varies.

Magnetic Trigger Circuits

Magnetic triggers use saturable reactors having inductance that can be varied. Controlling the current in a separate d-c control winding changes the permeability of the iron core. Direct current in the control winding saturates the core once during each half-cycle. This saturation has the effect of removing the core from the magnetic circuit at some point in the trigger cycle. The inductive reactance drops momentarily, permitting sufficient current in the gate circuit to trigger the SCR.

A typical magnetic trigger is shown in Fig. 4-13. Note that there are three distinct functions—power supply, control circuitry, and trigger circuitry. Transformer T1 is strictly a power transformer—it supplies the necessary voltage source for the trigger circuit and the main control circuit. The trigger circuit consists of the voltage just mentioned, a trigger winding on T2, a rectifier, and two resistors. With the rectifier in the circuit, the output will only be positive, as is desirable for the SCR gate. The impedance of the trigger winding on T2 varies with the magnetic flux in the transformer core. Until the core is saturated, current in the trigger circuit is limited to a value insufficient to fire the SCR. The resistors in

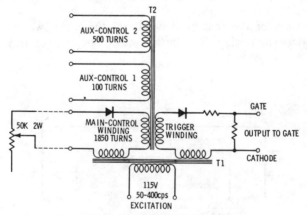

Fig. 4-13. Half-wave magnetic trigger.

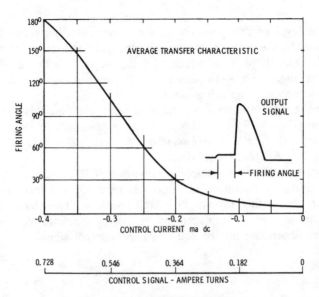

Fig. 4-14. Transfer characteristic.

the circuit are used to hold the amount of current and voltage available at the gate output to values suitable for triggering an SCR.

The main control circuit consists of a voltage source winding (on T1), a rectifier, and a potentiometer. The purpose of this circuit is to reduce the level of magnetic flux in the core of T2 below saturation on the negative half-cycle of the power supply.

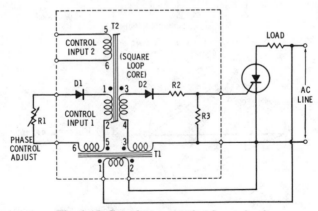

Fig. 4-15. Complete magnetic trigger circuit.

As the level of flux goes down, the trigger winding takes longer to saturate the core; consequently, the gate trigger pulse is delayed. Thus there is an increased firing angle or a deceased conduction angle. Fig. 4-14 shows the relationship between the control current and the firing angle.

Two alternate control windings are provided on this magnetic trigger (Fig. 4-13) that may be used in place of, or in conjunction with, the main control winding. An external source of power is required for these windings.

Fig. 4-15 shows a complete half-wave SCR circuit using magnetic firing. A common a-c supply is used for the load and the trigger, eliminating any synchronizing problems. The phase-control adjustment can be replaced by transistor circuitry or suitable sensor, depending on the source of the control signal.

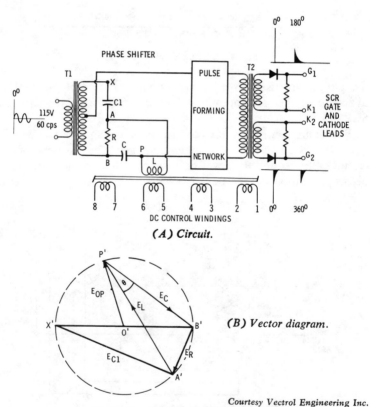

(A) Circuit.

(B) Vector diagram.

Courtesy Vectrol Engineering Inc.

Fig. 4-16. Silicontrol magnetic trigger.

A phase-shift magnetic amplifier is shown in Fig. 4-16A. This is a special patented form of wide-angle phase-shifting circuit controlled by a saturable reactor called *Silicontrol*. There is 180° range of linear phase shift using a small (4 milliwatt) d-c control signal to provide a steeply rising gate pulse.

The basic phase-shift mechanism may be seen in Fig. 4-16B. The a-c input feeds a fixed phase-shift network R-C1 to produce a base line voltage E_R across resistor R. Also across this resistor is a series resonant circuit, inductor L and capacitor C. The voltages across L and C are represented by vectors AP and BP.

When the inductance of L is altered slightly, the relative lengths of vectors AP and BP are effectively varied. Point P will, in effect, move around the dotted circle. The vector (O'P') then represents an output that can be taken from the network, varying in phase angle by approximately 300°, while remaining constant in amplitude.

Inductor L is a saturable reactor whose inductance is varied by saturating its core—passing varying amounts of direct current through the control windings. The output of this circuit then is formed into pulse spikes, which drive coupling transformer T2. Due to the blocking action of the two output diodes, positive spikes are delivered from gate lead G1 and from gate lead G2 on alternate half-cycles.

Circuit values are so adjusted that zero d-c control signal current (maximum inductive reactance in L) results in maximum phase delay (180°) and zero output from the SCR's. Maximum d-c input (4 milliwatts) means minimum inductance and minimum phase delay (maximum SCR output).

The multiple control inputs to the *Silicontrol* gate drive reactor permit almost unlimited design applications. These inputs may be parallel, or connected in series, or even connected in opposition to obtain the desired net resultant in the d-c control action. The several control windings can be used for performing functions useful in multiple feedback networks such as: voltage regulation, IR load current compensation, current limiting, anti-hunt stabilization, and line-voltage stabilization.

UNIJUNCTION TRANSISTORS

The unijunction transistor (Fig. 4-17) is a new and popular semiconductor device for providing pulses to fire SCR's. Its ad-

Courtesy International Rectifier Corp.

Fig. 4-17. Unijunction transistor.

vantages include satisfactory operation over a wide range of temperature, low current requirements for triggering (high input impedance), and ample output to trigger SCR's. Circuits using these devices are generally quite simple and compact; they have a very high power gain.

Theory of Operation

The unijunction transistor (abbreviated UJT) consists of a bar of n-type silicon with terminals at each end (base-1 and base-2) and an emitter of p-type silicon attached to the opposite side of the bar (Fig. 4-18A). The symbol for the UJT (Fig. 4-18B) looks very similar to the actual construction.

When voltages are applied to the UJT, as shown in Fig. 4-19, the silicon bar acts as a resistor through which a current (I_{B2}) flows from the battery (V_{BB}). The voltage divides across the bar (independent of temperature or current) so that a certain proportion of the battery voltage (V_{BB}) is present at the emitter-base junction. This is known as the peak-point voltage (V_P). The ratio

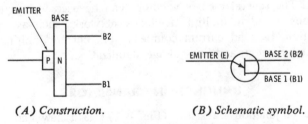

(A) Construction.   *(B) Schematic symbol.*

Fig. 4-18. Unijunction transistor.

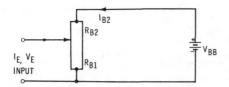

Fig. 4-19. Biasing of a
unijunction transistor.

of V_P to V_{BB} is called the intrinsic standoff ratio (μ). As long as V_P exceeds the signal voltage applied to the emitter (V_E), the emitter-base junction is reverse biased, and only a very small leakage current is present.

When the emitter voltage V_E) equals the peak-point voltage (V_P) (and the emitter current exceeds a value called the peak-point current), the junction will be forward biased and the UJT will turn on. The region from the emitter to base-one now exhibits a negative-resistance characteristic—the larger the current, the less the voltage drop (Fig. 4-20). The increase of charged carriers into the base also lowers the resistance from base-1 to base-2, so current I_{B2} increases greatly.

There are several uses for the UJT, but the basic circuit for firing the SCR is a relaxation oscillator (Fig. 4-21). In it the discharge current from the capacitor produces a positive pulse across a resistor that may be used to fire the SCR. The pulse decreases in amplitude as the temperature increases, which is an advantage in SCR firing circuits since the triggering requirements of the SCR also decrease with increasing temperature.

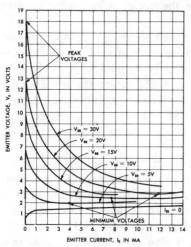

Fig. 4-20. Characteristics of a UJT.

Courtesy Texas Instruments Incorporated

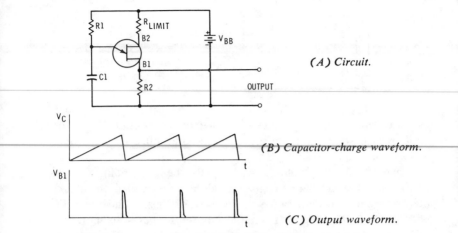

(A) Circuit.

(B) Capacitor-charge waveform.

(C) Output waveform.

Fig. 4-21. Relaxation oscillator.

Referring to Fig. 4-21, operation is as follows. Capacitor C1 charges at a rate determined by the time constant of R1 and C1. The voltage across C1 (on the emitter of the UJT) is shown in Fig. 4-21B. When this voltage reaches the peak-point voltage of the UJT, the latter fires. Capacitor C1 discharges through the emitter-base-1 circuit, producing the output pulse across R2 (Fig. 4-21C). It is this pulse that can be used to trigger an SCR.

Operation of the UJT is voltage-sensitive. By reducing either the base-to-base voltage (V_{BB}) or the supply voltage to base-1, the UJT can be fired at any part of the cycle. A transistor is often used to vary this voltage.

Where the unijunction is to be used to fire SCR's operating on alternating current, some method must be found to synchronize its oscillations with those of the supply frequency. A method for achieving this is illustrated in Fig. 4-22, where the input (base-to-base) voltage is either a half-wave or a full-wave rectified voltage. The zener diode clips it so that the input voltage at A appears as a square wave which drops to zero at the end of each half-cycle.

If the UJT has not fired by the end of the cycle, it will fire as the base-to-base voltage drops to zero. At some point the voltage stored in capacitor C will be greater than the voltage required to fire the unijunction, so the UJT will fire at the end of every cycle, discharging capacitor C to a fixed level. Since the UJT fires in the last few degrees of every cycle, it also fires the SCR. This may

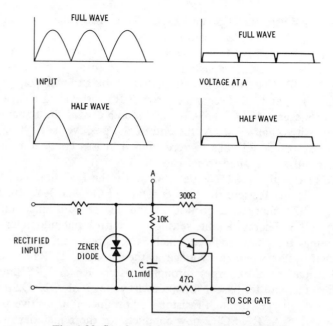

Fig. 4-22. Synchronizing a relaxation oscillator.

lead to a small current in the load of the SCR, but it usually can be neglected.

Typical Firing Circuits

Fig. 4-23 shows UJT's in a circuit used to fire SCR's. This provides full-wave phase control of the load current from 0 to 100

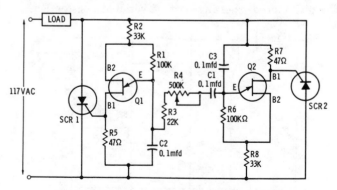

Fig. 4-23. Full-wave SCR control using UJT's.

per cent. Adjustment of potentiometer R4 controls the phase angle at which each controlled rectifier is fired.

During the positive half-cycle (when the voltage at the anode of SCR1 is positive), capacitor C2 charges through resistors R1 and R2 until it reaches the emitter-base-1 breakdown voltage of Q1. Q1 fires, and C2 discharges through R5, producing a positive pulse at the gate of SCR1. SCR1 now conducts for the remainder of the positive half-cycle. At the end of the positive half-cycle, the voltage across SCR1 falls to zero, and it ceases conducting until another pulse is applied to its gate.

The charge time of C2 is determined by the R-C time constant of C2, R1, and R2 and the time constant of C1, R3, R4, R6, and R8. (As C2 charges, a portion of the charge is drained off to charge C1.) Therefore, the setting of control potentiometer R4 determines the phase angle at which SCR1 fires. During the negative half-cycle (when the voltage at the anode of SCR1 is negative), capacitor C3 charges through resistors R6 and R8 until it reaches the emitter-base-1 breakdown voltage of Q2. Q2 fires, and C3 discharges through resistor R7, producing a positive pulse at the gate of SCR2. SCR2 now conducts for the remainder of the negative half-cycle. Again the charge time of C3 is controlled by R4—much as the charge time of C2 was controlled. The resulting voltage across the load is symmetrical, since the trigger circuits are identical.

Fig. 4-24 shows another UJT circuit providing a nonsymmetrical phase-control of the load current from 0 to 100 per cent. For half-wave phase control, switch S1A is in the right-hand position, placing diode D1 and resistor R2 across in series with the load. S1B is also closed, shorting part of variable resistor R4.

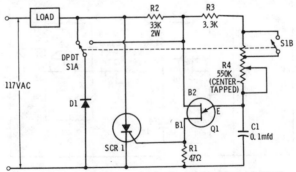

Fig. 4-24. Nonsymmetrical SCR control using a UJT.

During the negative half-cycle the power flows through D1, by-passing SCR1 and Q1, but almost all of it is dissipated in R2. During the positive half-cycle, capacitor C1 charges through resistors R3 and R4 until the charge equals the peak-point voltage of Q1. Q1 now fires, and C1 discharges through resistor R1, producing a positive pulse at the gate of SCR1. The latter continues to conduct until the end of the half-cycle, when the voltage across it drops to zero. For half-wave phase control, the charge time of C1, and hence the phase angle at which SCR1 fires, is determined by the R-C time constant of C1, R3, and potentiometer R4. Therefore, adjustment of R4 will provide phase control for half of the power cycle.

For full-wave phase control, switch S1A is placed in the left-hand position, connecting D1 in series with the load; S1B is open, placing the other half of R4 in series with C1. During the negative half-cycle, the current flows through the load and D1. During the positive half-cycle, capacitor C1 again charges through R3 and R4 (including the top half of R4)) until the charge equals the emitter-base-1 breakdown voltage of Q1. Q1 again fires, and a positive pulse triggers SCR1 into conduction as in the case for half-wave phase control. Again, adjustment of R4 controls the charge time of C1, thus controlling the phase angle at which SCR1 fires.

5

Motor Control

There are three general classes of motors based on their electrical construction and type of power used: universal, a-c, and d-c. Universal motors that can be operated on either a-c or d-c power are usually less than 1/25 horsepower. They are used to operate small appliances and hand tools—electric mixers, fans, blenders, drills, saws, and lathes—where their high torque at low speeds is a major feature. Speed control of these motors permits matching the motor to the load.

D-c motors are usually found in heavy-duty industrial applications where there is a need to control the speed. SCR's are rapidly finding a place in the control circuitry of these motors.

The speed of a-c motors is related to the frequency of the a-c power supply, so it is not practical to develop controls for varying the speed over a wide range. Control here usually consists of maintaining a constant speed in spite of power fluctuations. This can be done by varying the loading on the motor, and SCR's are used in circuitry for this purpose.

UNIVERSAL MOTORS

SCR's can easily be used for control of the universal motors found in household appliances and tools. As the load on a universal motor is increased, the motor slows down markedly; if the load is removed, the motor runs up to a high speed. For essentially constant speed characteristics with varying load, some type of feedback is necessary. Control is achieved by varying the con-

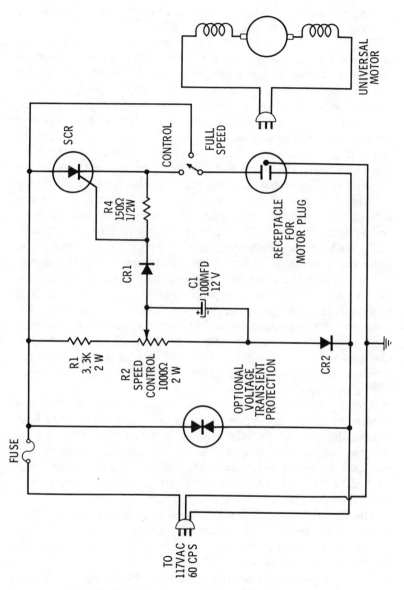

Fig. 5-1. Universal-motor speed control using back emf.

duction angle of the SCR, which, in turn, is determined by some characteristic of the motor associated with its operating speed. Current in the SCR gate circuit is a result of two factors; one is a voltage related to the setting on a speed control, and the other is a voltage developed by the motor itself.

Fig. 5-1 shows a universal motor control where the back emf developed by the motor is used to control the power supplied to the motor. In this circuit a switch is provided so that the motor can be operated directly across the line ("full speed"), or the speed may be varied by a potentiometer ("control").

Note that the gate circuit of the SCR contains two opposing voltage sources. The one on the arm of R2 (speed control) rises and falls at a fixed proportion of the line voltage during the positive half-cycles. The back emf developed by the motor is of the opposite polarity in the same circuit. The gate of the SCR cannot be triggered until the potentiometer voltage becomes positive enough to override the back emf. At slow motor speeds the back emf is small, so the SCR is triggered early in the positive half-cycle. At high speeds the back emf is large, and the conduction angle becomes small, reducing the power applied to the motor.

When a load is applied, the motor speed tends to decrease, and the counter emf decreases in proportion to the speed. The SCR triggers earlier in the cycle, applying additional voltage to the armature to compensate for the increased load and to maintain the desired speed. The particular speed at which the motor operates can be selected by R2. Stable operation is possible over approximately a 10-to-1 speed range. Stability at very low speeds can be improved by reducing the value of C1.

Rectifier CR1 prevents excessive reverse voltage on the gate of SCR, while R4 improves stability by bypassing commutator hash around the gate of the SCR and by reducing thermal effects on the triggering sensitivity of the SCR. The break-before-make action on the control switch prevents voltage transients from being applied to the SCR when the switch breaks the motor current in the full-speed position.

The circuit in Fig. 5-2 makes use of the motor residual field to induce an emf in the armature proportional to the speed. This voltage is employed as the speed feedback signal. Note that only the motor armature is in the SCR gate circuit.

This is a patented circuit developed by Momberg and Taylor of the Singer Manufacturing Company. The SCR is connected

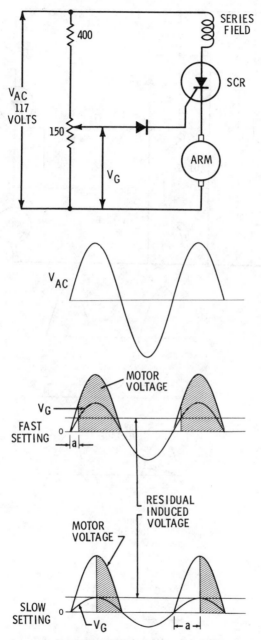

Fig. 5-2. Universal-motor speed control using residual field.

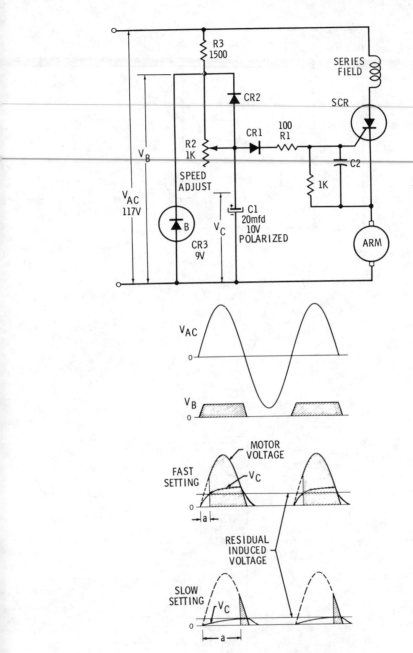

Fig. 5-3. Alternate circuit for Fig. 5-2.

between the field windings and the armature; a diode and two resistances complete the circuit. Voltage V_G is tapped off a potentiometer connected directly across the line and is thus an attenuated sine wave in phase with the voltage across the SCR in the blocking state (the source voltage V_{AC}). As the motor rotates the trigger signal voltage V_G is opposed in the gate circuit by the emf developed because of the residual field.

When the motor armature is standing still, no voltage is induced in the armature by the residual field, and the SCR fires early in the cycle, providing ample armature voltage to accelerate the motor. As the motor speeds up, its residual induced voltage increases in proportion to its speed. This voltage on the armature bucks the flow of gate current and requires that voltage V_G reach a higher value before the SCR will fire. The firing angle is automatically increased, allowing the motor to reach a stable equilibrium speed.

When a load is applied to the motor, the speed tends to decrease, reducing the residual induced voltage in the armature. This automatically reduces the firing angle, giving more power and increasing motor torque. Thus the motor speed remains essentially constant in spite of the increased load.

Note the waveforms (Fig. 5-2) when the potentiometer arm is in a high-speed position. V_G reaches a relatively large amplitude, firing the SCR early in the cycle. In the low-speed setting the amplitude of V_G is small, so the SCR fires approximately at the midpoint in the cycle.

This simple circuit is limited by the fact that the SCR cannot be consistently fired at a firing angle greater than $90°$; consequently, operation at very low speeds is not stable. The circuit also has a tendency to hunt with line-voltage variations when operating around a $90°$ firing angle.

Where stable operation at very low speeds is required, the circuit of Fig. 5-3 is suggested. This circuit also relies on the residual induced field for a speed feedback signal, but a very short conduction time for the SCR (and thus a very slow speed) is possible.

During the negative half-cycle of the supply voltage, capacitor C1 is discharged to zero; during the positive half-cycle, C1 charges from a constant potential (the zener voltage of CR3) at an exponential rate dependent on the time constant R2-C1. V_{AC} is the source voltage, V_B is the voltage across the zener diode, and V_C is the voltage across C1.

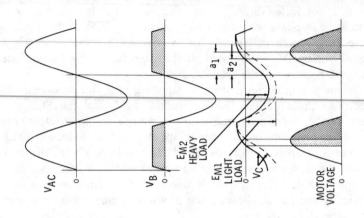

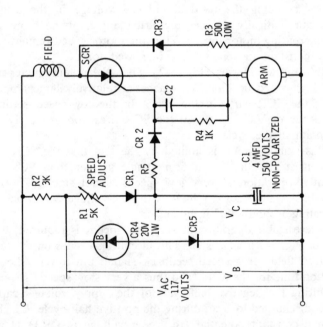

Fig. 5-4. Universal-motor speed control using induced armature
voltage to discharge capacitor.

When the motor armature is standing still, no voltage is induced in it by the residual field. Gate current to the SCR flows as soon as V_C exceeds the forward voltage drop of CR1 and the gate drop of the SCR. This will fire the SCR early in the cycle.

As the motor approaches the speed set on the control, the residual induced voltage in the armature builds up. This voltage is positive on the top terminal of the armature so it blocks the flow of gate current from capacitor C1 until V_C exceeds the armature voltage. The higher the voltage requirement on C1, the longer it takes, so the firing angle is retarded, allowing the motor to cease accelerating.

After the motor has reached operating speed, the residual induced voltage provides automatic speed regulation. For example, if a heavy load starts to reduce the motor speed, the induced voltage decreases, causing the SCR to fire earlier in the cycle. Additional energy is furnished to the motor to supply the necessary torque for the increased load. Also, a light load, with its tendency to increase speed, raises the motor residual induced voltage, retarding the firing angle and reducing the voltage on the motor.

R2 adjusts the desired speed by controlling the charging rate of capacitor C1. When R2 is adjusted to a low value, V_C builds up quickly and fires the SCR early in the cycle. When R2 is set to a large value, V_C builds up slowly so that firing occurs late in the cycle; therefore the motor speed is low.

Fig. 5-4 shows another circuit where the SCR is connected between field windings and the armature. Instead of relying on the negative half-cycle of line voltage to discharge capacitor C1, the induced armature emf is used for this purpose. When the line voltage is negative, the series field is excited through R3 and CR3, inducing a negative voltage in the armature that is proportional to the speed of the motor and the field strength. The negative armature voltage charges capacitor C1 through CR2 and the SCR gate so that the top terminal of C1 becomes negative with respect to the bottom. As the line voltage swings positive, C1 discharges and then charges to the reverse polarity through R1 at a rate dependent on the R1-C1 time constant. When the trigger voltage is reached, the SCR is fired. Line voltage is now applied to the motor.

The dashed curve of V_C shows the circuit under lightly loaded conditions. V_C reaches a peak negative value of E_{M1}, and triggers the SCR at firing angle α_1. If a heavy load is applied to the motor, it tends to slow down. This reduces the induced armature voltage and limits the peak negative value of V_C to E_{M2}. V_C thus discharges sooner than under no load conditions, swinging positive and triggering the SCR at a firing angle of α_2. This decrease in the firing angle increases the voltage applied to the motor and delivers additional torque to the motor to compensate for the increased load.

Zener regulator CR4 provides a constant voltage for the recharging of C1, allowing the circuit to be controlled smoothly down to almost standstill. The desired speed is adjusted by R1. C2 and R4 are connected from gate to cathode of the SCR to stabilize the circuit by preventing the SCR from being fired by extraneous signals.

Various other gate-firing devices and circuits are possible using the a-c line to deliver firing pulses during each positive half-cycle. These vary the timing of the pulses in proportion to a small d-c control voltage.

Many circuit designs are based on the fact that the speed of a universal motor is proportional to the ratio of armature voltage to field current, neglecting saturation and armature resistance (corrections for these can be incorporated in a control system). The SCR is often connected through a series resistor between the single-phase a-c supply and the motor terminals so as to rectify the input voltage and supply a controlled output to the motor. The SCR gate is controlled by any suitable gate trigger, which varies the output of the SCR in accordance with the d-c voltage applied to the d-c control terminals of the trigger. When the control voltage is zero, the conduction angle of the gate pulses is reduced, and the SCR output is low; as the control voltage is increased, the gate-pulse conduction angle is increased, and the SCR output is increased. An error signal developed across the trigger control terminals automatically controls the SCR output so that sufficient voltage is applied to the motor to maintain speed.

D-C SHUNT MOTORS

The most versatile motor for industrial variable-speed applications is the d-c shunt motor. The speed can be changed by adjusting the armature voltage while the field excitation is held constant.

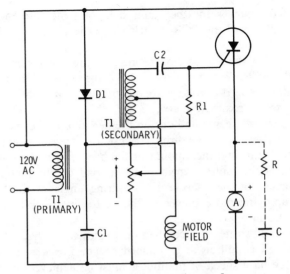

Fig. 5-5. D-c motor speed control.

With this arrangement, the shunt motor can supply the same torque throughout its variable-speed range as it does at its base speed.

One SCR circuit for shunt-wound (or permanent magnet field) d-c motors is the schematic in Fig. 5-5. This SCR circuit is limited to certain low-power SCR types requiring only a small gate current to fire. Such a circuit can be used in motors in the sub-fractional horsepower range of from 1/100 hp downward.

The SCR trigger is an a-c voltage obtained from the secondary of transformer T1 and delayed in phase by the C2-R1 network. In order to vary the firing angle, a d-c voltage is added to the a-c trigger. This direct current is provided by rectifier D1, which also

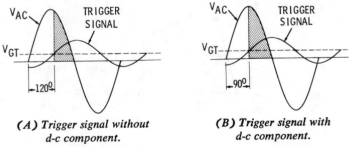

(A) Trigger signal without d-c component.

(B) Trigger signal with d-c component.

Fig. 5-6. Varying the trigger point by using a d-c voltage.

furnishes d-c power for the shunt field. An increase in the d-c voltage will cause the SCR to trigger earlier, thus speeding the motor.

In Fig. 5-6 the dotted line represents the voltage required to trigger the SCR. Without a d-c voltage the SCR might trigger at 120°; adding the d-c voltage to the trigger signal could advance the firing to approximately 90°.

The back emf (generated during the negative half-cycle, and the positive half-cycle before firing) bucks the trigger voltage when the motor is turning; the amount of the back emf is determined by the speed of the motor. An increase of load on the motor results in a decrease of the back emf. The firing angle of the SCR advances, applying more power to the motor in order to keep the speed constant.

Fig. 5-7 illustrates the conduction angles for a typical no-load and full-load condition at a reduced speed. For a well-regulated system, the base speed of the motor must be achieved with a conduction angle considerably less than 90°. This is necessary so that the load voltage at the time the SCR fires will increase as the load is increased. If the SCR fired at 90°, adding a load would increase the conduction angle to allow for a greater power output,

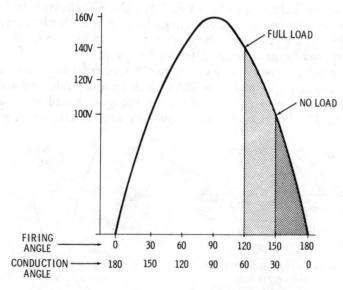

Fig. 5-7. Variation in firing and conduction angles with loading.

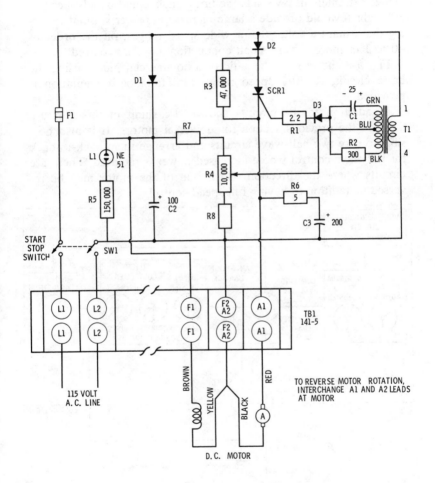

Fig. 5-8. Commercial d-c motor controller.

79

but the firing would occur at a reduced voltage, causing a reduced speed.

The peak sine voltage is 160 volts for the 115-volt line; if the base motor speed at no load is calculated at 150° firing angle, a motor-armature voltage rating of 80 volts would be required. Under extremely heavy loads the firing angle could be advanced to 30°, which would provide a large increase in power without reducing the armature voltage. For wide speed ranges, on the order of 40 to 1 or more, a very small conduction angle is required.

Fig. 5-8 shows the schematic of a commercial model using the basic circuit. A 20/1 speed range with fair speed regulation is provided.

In addition to the circuits shown, d-c shunt motors can use those in the previous section for universal motors. It is also possible to take two half-wave circuits and arrange them back-to-back for full-wave control where increased power is required. There are circuits where the direction of rotation of the motor may be reversed in addition to having full speed control.

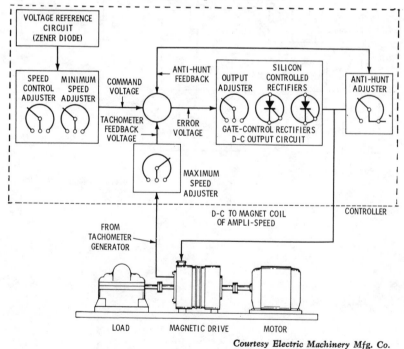

Courtesy Electric Machinery Mfg. Co.

Fig. 5-9. *Ampli-Speed* magnetic drive system.

A-C MOTOR CONTROL

A-c motor control is quite different from d-c motor control. There is no simple and direct mode for this, since the motor speed is related to the frequency of the a-c source.

The *Ampli-Speed* in Fig. 5-9 is an example of a system of precise a-c speed control for electrical drive applications. It consists of (1) the magnetic drive operated by a constant speed motor, (2) the controller circuitry (inside the box), and (3) a pilot or actuating device which prescribes the speed to be maintained or adjusted. The system can be used with various transducers, voltage signals, or other auxiliary components to provide speed control, relieve overload, and establish the torque limit.

The magnetic drive consists of a rotating ring member and a rotating magnet in a self-contained structure. Each has a shaft, and each rotates independently. The ring and magnet have an airgap between them which is maintained by a pair of inner bearings. The ring is driven by a motor, revolving at motor speed or at some multiple of it.

The magnet is coupled by gears or belts to the load. Slip rings are mounted on the magnet shaft for the input of excitation current to the magnet winding, and a tachometer generator is mounted on the magnet shaft. The tachometer generates a voltage proportional to the speed of the shaft. The entire rotating assembly is mounted on a frame with main bearings for support.

The motor is connected to the load by the magnetic drive, which is an electromagnetic torque transmitter. Torque is produced by the reaction between the magnetic field of the magnet and eddy current magnetism induced across the airgap in the ring. The strength of the magnetic field is determined by the amount of excitation current. The current also determines the amount of magnetism induced in the ring, and hence the amount of reaction. Output torque is therefore regulated by the amount of d-c excitation to the magnet. This excitation current is supplied by the controller.

Circuitry for the *Ampli-Speed* controller is shown in Fig. 5-10. The controller converts a single-phase, 120-volt input into a controlled d-c current that is fed through the slip rings to the magnet field winding. Variation in this current provides variation in the intensity of the magnetic field, which in turn determines the amount of torque transmitted.

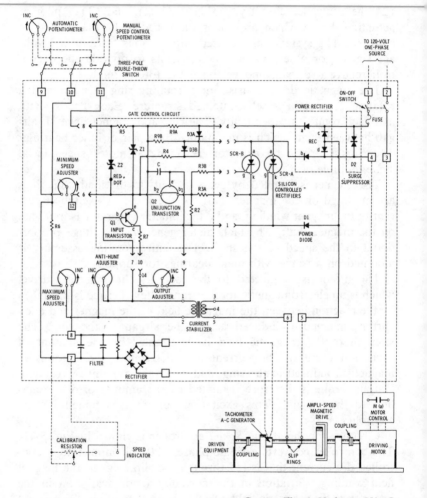

Courtesy Electric Machinery Mfg. Co.

Fig. 5-10. *Ampli-Speed* **circuitry.**

The controller responds to an activating signal which creates a command voltage. This is compared to the tachometer-generator feedback voltage to produce an error voltage. At steady speed this error voltage is zero; a change in the relation of command to feedback voltage, either up or down, changes the error voltage since this a closed-loop servo system.

The a-c input is 120 volt, single phase; REC is a full-wave bridge using diodes c and d and SCR's A and B. Diodes a and b are in series with the SCR's, so the peak inverse voltage ratings will not be exceeded. The gate control circuit fires the SCR's through a gate signal applied to g.

Diode D1 is the commutating diode for field discharge current at the end of each half-cycle (when an SCR stops conduction). After the gate fires an SCR, it stays on until the anode voltage goes to zero. Once the SCR fires (conducts current), control by the gate is not regained until the anode current diminishes below a value called the holding current. D1, the commutating diode, provides a path for the field discharge current at the end of each half-cycle, when the voltage input goes through zero. At this time the anode current of the conducting SCR drops below the holding current, and the gate has a half-cycle to regain control before the next half-cycle of forward voltage is applied.

Zener diode Z1 limits this voltage, which is applied to transistor Q1 and unijunction Q2. Gate firing signals are obtained by discharge of C through Q2 when the charge on C exceeds the emitter to base-one voltage of Q2.

The charging rate of the capacitor is dependent on the collector current of transistor Q1, which, in turn, is controlled by the value of the base current. A maximum collector current limit is determined by the setting of the Output Adjuster. In this way the transistor base current controls the rate of capacitor voltage built-up and through that controls the length of the nonconducting period for each half-cycle.

Since each half-cycle is a fixed time period, control of the quiescent period gives control of the conducting period which results in control of the output to the magnetic drive. Input is the base current of Q1; output is the remainder of the power sine waves after the quiescent period. An increase in Q1 base current gives an increase in output.

The command voltage is the direct current output of a potentiometer system connected across low-voltage reference zener diode, Z2. The potentiometer system is composed of two potentiometers and the Minimum Speed Adjuster. Voltage from terminals 12 to 10 is the command voltage, and is a fraction of the low-voltage power supply across Z2.

The feedback voltage is that part of the tachometer generator voltage appearing between terminal 7 and the tap of the Maximum Speed Adjuster. Error voltage is the command voltage minus the tachometer feedback voltage. During normal steady-state operation the error voltage is about zero for the quiescent period. During the conducting period the error voltage is the full feedback voltage, but then it has no effect on the output.

Typical action occurs when the speed control potentiometer is adjusted for a higher speed point. This increases the command voltage, giving an error voltage that produces a higher base current in Q1. The resulting high output from the SCR's is applied to the *Ampli-Speed* field, increasing the torque output to the load. The load speed increases until the tachometer feedback voltage is high enough again to balance the command voltage to a near-zero error. There must, however, be enough error voltage to maintain the output required to hold the load at the new speed point.

Any tendency to hunt about the set speed can be counteracted with the introduction of the anti-hunt feedback signal from the current stabilizer. The amount of anti-hunt signal is set with the anti-hunt adjuster.

6

Applications of the SCR

When the size of an SCR is compared to the size of the devices it can replace (thyratrons, mechanical switches, tube rectifiers, rheostats) it is easy to understand why they are now being used in such a wide variety of circuits. Only the cost differential is a major limiting factor. As production increases and manufacturing techniques improve, even this drawback will disappear.

LIGHTING CONTROL

SCR's can be used to adjust the light level of incandescent lamps. Proportional power-control methods are used to provide adjustable lighting with silicon controlled rectifiers. Commercial units are available in a wide variety of ratings that will handle many types of loads besides lighting. A typical unit is shown in Fig. 6-1.

Simple Full-Wave Control

Fig. 6-2 shows a simple full-wave control circuit adaptable to lighting control. The size of the load that can be handled will depend on the rating of the SCR's used. Operation of the circuit is as follows. When neither SCR is conducting, capacitor C1 charges on the positive half-cycle of the power source at a rate determined by the time constant of R2, R1, and C1. When C1 charges sufficiently, it triggers SCR1 into conduction; the latter will continue to conduct until the end of the positive half-cycle. Since R1 is variable, the length of time required to charge C1 can be regulated. The conduction angle of SCR1 varies accordingly.

Courtesy International Resistance Company
Fig. 6-1. A solid-state power control.

The charge on capacitor C2 is used to trigger SCR2. However, on the positive half-cycle, C2 charges (while SCR1 is turned off) to the reverse polarity of that required to trigger. When the power-source polarity reverses (negative half-cycle), capacitor C2 must be discharged and then charged in the opposite direction before it can trigger SCR2. This action keeps the conduction angle of both SCR's about the same. If SCR1 conducts for the full half-cycle, C2 is not reverse charged, so it quickly triggers CR2

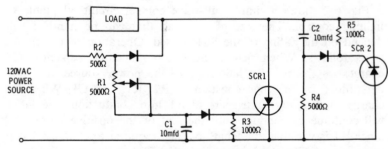

Fig. 6-2. Full-wave lamp dimmer.

86

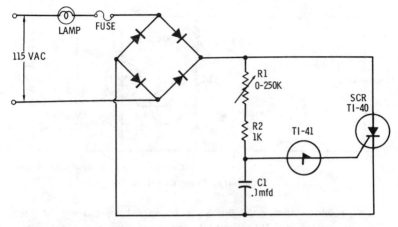

Courtesy Texas Instruments Incorporated

Fig. 6-3. Full-wave bridge control.

into conduction. If SCR1 conducts for only a small portion of the half-cycle, C2 will have a large reverse charge to be overcome before it can trigger SCR2.

Full-Wave Bridge Circuit

The full-wave bridge circuit in Fig. 6-3, which permits control from zero to full brilliance, uses a 4-layer diode as well as an SCR. The output of the full-wave bridge is fed into the SCR control circuit so that one SCR controls both halves of an a-c cycle.

R1, R2, and C1 are selected to make the voltage across C1 lag the input by 60° when R1 is at maximum. The amplitude of this voltage must be sufficient to break down the 4-layer diode so there will be a pulse coming from the capacitor through the diode to fire the SCR at about 150°. Even though this is the lowest light level setting, a pulse will be applied to the load twice each cycle; these pulses will be small and may cause the lamp to glow very slightly. It is necessary that the 4-layer diode fire each half-cycle, discharging the capacitor, in order to prevent lamp flicker due to intermittent firing of the SCR at advanced firing angles.

The voltage across capacitor C will build up faster as R1 is decreased. This action will fire the SCR earlier in the cycle and apply more power to the lamp. The controlled rectifier can be made to fire at any point in the cycle between 15° and 150° by varying R1.

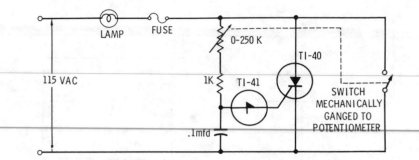

Fig. 6-4. Half-wave control.

To prevent damage to the SCR by inrush of current at cold filament conditions, R1 should be at maximum resistance when the power source is switched on. This will also allow a conservative rating for the fuse protecting against short circuits.

Half-Wave Circuit

The operation of the half-wave circuit in Fig. 6-4 is similar to the previous full-wave circuit, except that proportional control is possible only from off to half brilliance. For full brilliance, the switch is closed to short out the control circuitry. This arrangement allows continuous control from zero to half power and a step from half to full power.

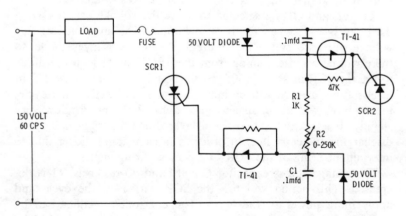

Fig. 6-5. Full-wave control.

This circuit is simple and has only a small number of components; it also eliminates the flickering problem. The capacitor is able to discharge on each negative half-cycle even if the 4-layer diode trigger has not fired, preventing premature firing on the next positive half-cycle.

Full-Wave Power-Control Circuit

Fig. 6-5 is a full-wave power-control circuit providing a continuously variable, symmetrical output; this may be used to replace magnetic amplifiers, autotransformers, thyratrons, ignitrons, and relays. It is very similar to the circuit of Fig. 6-2, except for the use of 4-layer diodes in place of regular diodes.

Each half of the a-c cycle is controlled by a separate controlled rectifier. SCR1 is fired when its anode becomes positive and the current through R1 and R2 charges C1 to a sufficient value to break down the 4-layer diode in series with the gate of SCR1. The other half of the a-c cycle is controlled by SCR2, which is fired in the same manner. The point in the cycle at which the controlled rectifiers are fired can be controlled by adjusting R2, thus changing the R-C time constant of the firing circuit.

EMERGENCY LIGHTING SYSTEM

Emergency lighting systems are used in many public places; Fig. 6-6 is a schematic for a unit that provides battery-operated

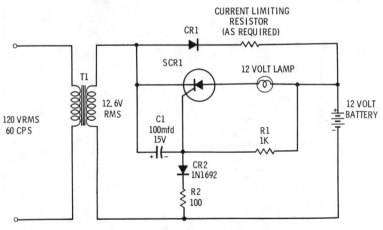

Fig. 6-6. Emergency lighting circuit.

emergency lighting instantaneously and automatically upon failure of the 120-volt power. When normal services is resumed, the emergency light is extinguished, and the battery is recharged in preparation for the next time it is needed.

When a-c power is present, capacitor C1 charges through diode CR2 and resistor R2 and discharges through resistor R1 and the battery. Because the discharge time constant is longer than the charging time constant, C1 retains a net positive charge. This charge reverse-biases the SCR gate so that it cannot fire. At the same time, the battery is being charged through rectifier CR1. Circuitry can be added to prevent overcharging the battery.

Should the a-c power fail, C1 discharges completely and then starts to charge in the opposite direction, since it is in series with the battery. When the voltage on C1 is sufficient to trigger SCR1, the latter turns on and energizes the emergency 12-volt lamp. Reset is automatic when alternating current is restored, because the SCR will be reverse biased. When CR1 conducts to charge the battery, the anode of the SCR will be less positive (or more negative) than the cathode due to the voltage drop across the current-limiting resistor.

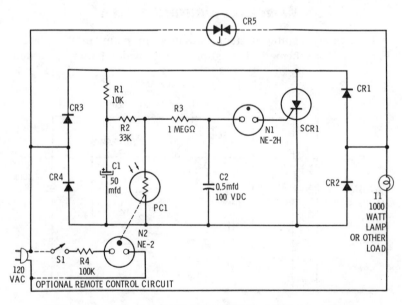

Fig. 6-7. Lamp-flasher circuit—activated by the absence of light.

Fig. 6-7 shows a lamp flasher operating from a-c power, which can control up to 1000 watts for warning lights. Other devices (incandescent lamps, sirens, or motors) may be used. Operation of the circuit can be started automatically when the sun goes down and turned off at dawn when the sun goes up.

There are four rectifiers forming a bridge with an SCR across the bridge. The load (1000-watt lamp) is in the a-c line and is turned on when the SCR fires. The SCR is triggered by a pulse from neon lamp N1, which must have 90 volts across it to fire. This is provided by the charging of capacitor C2. When the SCR is not conducting, the voltage across the bridge is about 150 volts, and C2, in series with R1, R2, and R3, charges toward this value.

The charging of C2 is limited by the presence of photoconductor PC1, connected at the junction of R2 and R3. Light shining on PC1 lowers its resistance so that the voltage at the junction of R2 and R3 is lowered below the firing level of neon lamp N1. However, when PC1 is in the dark, its resistance is high, and the neon can fire. Thus the SCR can be fired only when there is no light shining on PC1.

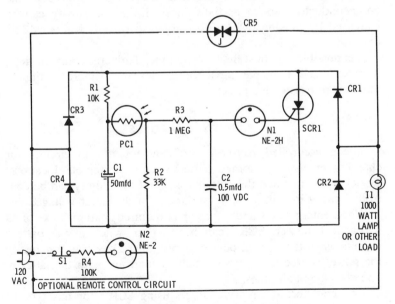

Fig. 6-8. Lamp-flasher circuit—activated by light.

Without capacitor C1 in the circuit, the SCR would conduct only a half-cycle before turning off since it is across rectified alternate current that drops to zero every half-cycle. C1 is added to prolong the conduction period. When the SCR is nonconducting, C1 charges toward the peak value of the supply voltage, 150 volts. When the SCR fires, current from C1 holds the SCR is conduction until C1 is completely discharged. The length of the conducting period of the SCR (and the flash of the lamp) can be varied by changing the value of C1.

It is also possible to use remote control by adding a second neon lamp (N2) and adjusting a mask for photocell PC1 so that it will only be activated by the light from neon lamp N2. This will provide a sensitive remote control completely isolated from the load circuit itself. If low-voltage remote control is desired, a flashlight lamp can be used instead of the neon bulb. The lamp should be operated at about 50% of the rated voltage to provide long life.

The circuit can be inverted so that it will flash when the photoconductor is illuminated instead of when the photoconductor is dark. Fig. 6-8 shows how this is done; PC1 and R2 are interchanged in the circuit. To decrease the sensitivity to light the photoconductor can be partially masked. The sensitivity can be increased by making resistor R2 larger so that it is about 470K ohms.

It is possible to adjust the flashing time. To increase the on time, it is necessary to make capacitor C1 larger; to increase the off time, make resistor R3 larger.

BATTERY CHARGERS

Silicon controlled rectifiers are ideal for use in circuits for charging emergency storage batteries used in remote locations. The charging rate and the output voltage of the battery can be controlled easily in spite of wide variations in the input voltage.

When emergency standby power is required, batteries are often a practical answer. SCR's can be used to switch in the battery circuits when the normal power supply fails. They can also rectify the power source to charge the battery, and maintain the latter in a ready state at all times.

Two commercial battery chargers using SCR's for this type of service are pictured in Fig. 6-9.

(A) Rack mounted.

(B) Free standing.

Fig. 6-9. Battery chargers.

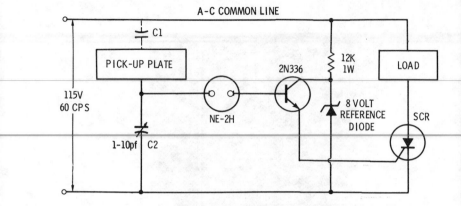

Fig. 6-10. Proximity switch using a pick-up plate.

ALARM CIRCUITS

Fig. 6-10 is a proximity switch designed to detect any approaching objects. The circuit uses the capacity between the object being detected and "earth" ground as the input.

The capacity between ground and the pick-up plate form capacitor C1. This and variable capacitor C2 are a capacitive divider across the a-c line. The ratio of C1 to C2 determines the voltage applied to the neon bulb. The sensitivity of this circuit can be set by adjusting variable capacitor C2.

The capacity to the pick-up plate increases when the plate approaches or is approached by another object. This increases

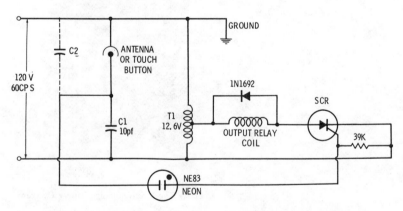

Fig. 6-11. Proximity switch using a touch button or an antenna.

the voltage on the neon bulb to a sufficient value to make it fire. When the neon bulb fires, capacitors C1 and C2 discharge very rapidly through the base of the transistor. A capacitance of less than 10 picofarads will produce a pulse of current of several hundred microamps. The current pulse, amplified by the transistor, is used to fire the controlled rectifier. The SCR, once fired, will remain on only until the a-c voltage reverses polarity and turns the SCR off. However, it will continue to fire each cycle as long as the capacitance-producing object remains near, so there will be pulsating direct current through the load. The 12K-ohm resistor and the zener diode provide collector voltage for the transistor amplifier.

Fig. 6-11 is another version of the proximity switch. The pick-up plate is replaced by an antenna or a touch button, and the load consists of the coil of a relay. No transistor amplifier is required for the gate pulse in this case; the neon lamp triggers the SCR directly.

Latching action can be achieved if desired by driving only the SCR anode circuit with direct current. Sensitivity of the arrangement is a function both of sensing distance and sensor plate size; the plate can be made smaller in area if the sensing distance is small. For a touch control the sensing plate need be no bigger than a penny.

A variety of automatic alarm circuit arrangements can be made from the basic relaxation-oscillator circuit of Fig. 6-12A. In it a single controlled rectifier drives a speaker or earphones from a 22.5-volt battery source.

This circuit is different from some in that the increase of voltage on the anode and the gate instead of the gate alone is used to fire the SCR. When switch S1 is closed, C1 charges. The voltage on the anode of the SCR rises with that on the capacitor; a portion of this voltage, determined by the setting of R2, is applied to the gate. When the proper combination of anode and gate voltage is reached, the SCR fires, discharging capacitor C1 through the speaker. Resistor R1 limits the circuit current below the holding current for the SCR, so the SCR turns off when the capacitor is discharged. This cycle repeats as long as the switch is closed, producing a low-frequency tone in the speaker.

A cadmium sulphide photoconductor is used in Fig. 6-12B. In this example resistor R2 is adjusted at the threshold of oscillation; any slight increase in the amount of light on the photoconduc-

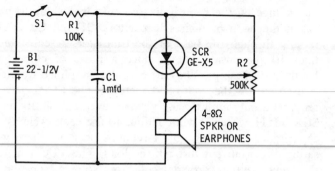

(A) Switch triggered.

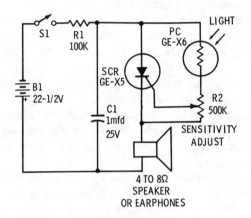

(B) Light triggered.

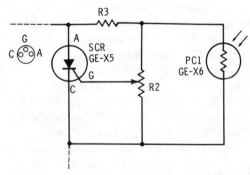

Courtesy General Electric Co.

(C) Darkness triggered.

Fig. 6-12. Relaxation-oscillator alarm circuit.

tor will cause an output. In Fig. 6-12C a reversed mode of operation is shown where reduction in the amount of light produces an output.

It is also possible to use a high-resistance thermistor, one having a value of about 100,000 ohms at ordinary room temperature. A thermistor used in this manner can detect over-temperature with this circuit. Similarly, a humidity sensor can be used to detect changes in humidity, and a ceramic or crystal microphone can detect vibrations or changes in noise level.

It is also possible to use this alarm to detect smoke, utilizing the smoke detector shown in Fig. 6-13. The inside of the chimney, as well as the collar and cup, should be painted black in order to reduce the reflected light. Heat from the lamp creates flow of the room air through the chimney. If there is smoke in the air, light will be reflected from the smoke into the photoconductor to activate the alarm. It is necessary that the photoconductor be shielded both from the heat and from direct light.

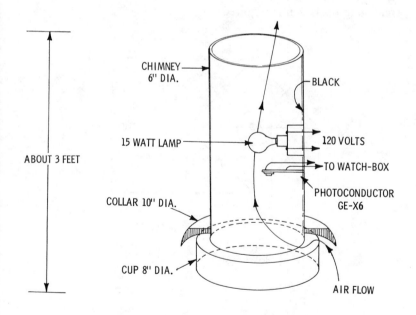

Courtesy General Electric Co.

Fig. 6-13. Cross-section of a smoke detector.

TEMPERATURE CONTROL

The SCR, when tied to a sensitive transducer, can provide a control output as a function of temperature. Fig. 6-14 shows a circuit where the SCR serves both as a current amplifier for the mercury thermostat and as the main-load switching element. When the thermostat is open, the SCR triggers each half-cycle, delivering power to the heater load. When the thermostat closes, however, the SCR can no longer trigger, and the heater shuts off. Current through the thermostat is less than one ma rms.

This type of inverted operation—conducting when there is no signal, cutting off when a signal is present—takes advantages of the characteristics of the low-current SCR. When the SCR is required to block voltage (heater off), its gate is essentially shorted to the cathode, which is an extremely stable operating mode. When the SCR is required to trigger, however, there is no shunting resistance between gate and cathode to reduce the effective input sensitivity of the device. Heat-sensitive semiconductor switching devices can take the place of the mercury thermostat with equal efficiency if all solid-state operation is required.

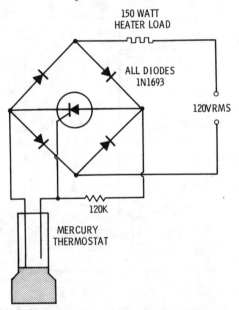

Fig. 6-14. Temperature controller operated
by a mercury thermostat.

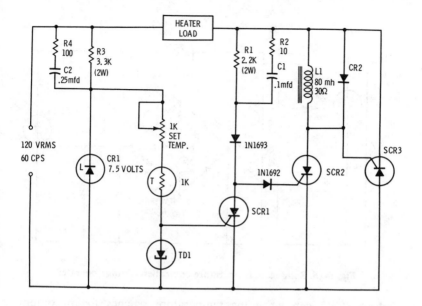

Fig. 6-15. Solid-state temperature controller.

Fig. 6-15 shows a precision temperature control. This circuit will deliver approximately 5 kilowatts to a heater load, and maintain the temperature within 1°F of the set point. The thermistor required should have a resistance of approximately 1000 ohms at the desired set point. With SCR1 nonconducting, SCR2 is anode fired each alternate half-cycle by the combination of R1, R2, and C1. R2 and C1 ensure that SCR2 triggers early in the cycle to minimize radio interference noise. At the end of each half-cycle that SCR2 conducts, energy stored in choke L1 freewheels through the gate of SCR3 for a sufficient time to ensure that SCR3 triggers as the line voltage reverses. Because SCR3 triggers at the start of the negative half-cycles, r-f interference is minimized. Diode CR2 prevents excessive dissipation in L1, allowing a physically small choke to be used for L1.

The thermistor monitors the temperature of the load being powered by SCR2 and SCR3. As the load temperature rises, the thermistor resistance drops; there is more current in the tunnel diode and SCR gate circuit. When this current is sufficient to trigger TD1, SCR1 also is triggered, shorting the gate of SCR2 to its cathode. The circuit is designed so that SCR1 always fires

99

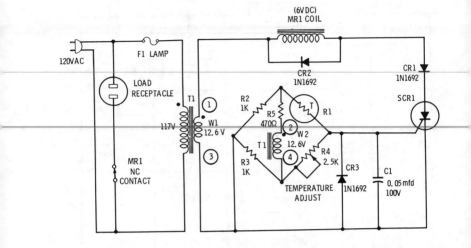

Fig. 6-16. Solid-state temperature controller—bridge operated.

before SCR2 can when the temperature reaches the maximum desired. Power is thus removed from the load until the thermistor resistance increases sufficiently for tunnel diode TD1 to stop triggering each cycle. TD1 is reset each alternate half-cycle by the negative line voltage.

Another circuit where a thermistor can be used to advantage for temperature control is shown in Fig. 6-16. Transformer T1 has two secondary windings: W1 furnishes voltage to the coil of relay MR1 (which controls the load) through SCR1, and W2 furnishes a-c voltage to the trigger circuit of SCR1. Temperature-sensing thermistor R1 is electrically connected into a bridge with R2, R3, and adjusting potentiometer R4. When the resistance of thermistor R1 equals the resistance setting on R4, the bridge is balanced, and none of the a-c voltage introduced into the bridge by winding W2 is applied to the gate of SCR1. Hence, relay MR1 remains de-energized, and its normally closed contacts apply power to the heating elements connected to the load receptacle.

If the temperature increases, the resistance of thermistor R1 decreases, unbalancing the bridge in a direction such that there is trigger current to SCR1 while its anode is positive. This turns on SCR1 and energizes the relay, disconnecting power from the load receptacle. Below the preset temperature setting, R1 unbalances the bridge in the opposite direction, so a negative signal is applied

100

to the gate of SCR 1 when its anode is positive. The SCR cannot turn on, so power continues to flow to the heating elements.

In the previous circuit the bridge unbalance had to be in one certain direction to trigger the SCR. In Fig. 6-17, however, the circuit is designed so that the SCR triggers no matter in which direction the bridge is unbalanced.

When positive gate voltage coincides with negative voltage at B, for instance, load current flows through load No. 1 and diode CRI; when positive gate voltage coincides with negative voltage at A, load current flows through load No. 2 and diode CR2. When the bridge is balanced, both loads will remain turned off. This circuit is suited for temperature monitoring, warning systems, and similar applications where the dual-load output feature can be used to drive temperature-indicator lamps.

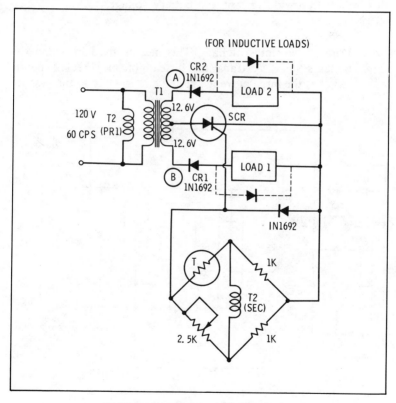

Fig. 6-17. Phase-sensitive switch.

TRANSISTOR IGNITION SYSTEMS

From the first automobile ignition system the problems of points pitting and poor voltage output at high speeds has been recognized. The heavy current across the contacts causes wear and surface erosion, both of which cause points to require replacement. At high speeds the voltage output drops sharply, causing incomplete ignition and a waste of fuel. Although electronic ignition systems have been possible for a long time, it is only the transistor which has made rugged, efficient systems with no warm-up possible.

Three techniques are available for using semiconductors in automotive ignition systems. The main requirement is a properly timed spark of from 15 to 35 kilovolts that has a peak spark power of about 900 watts. All three of the following systems can provide this even with a wide variation in battery voltage.

The three systems are:

1. Primary current switching. This can be used in a conventional system. A transistor instead of the breaker points switches the large currents, giving a longer life to the system.

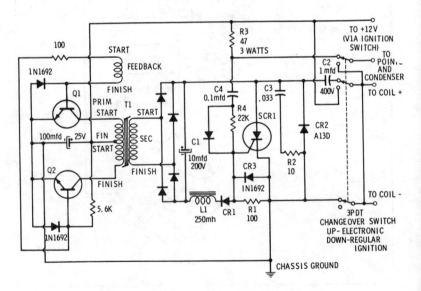

Fig. 6-18. Capacitor-discharge ignition system.

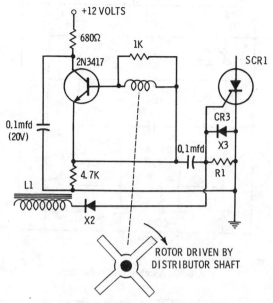

Fig. 6-19. Eliminating auto breaker points.

2. Energy storage. A transistor switch discharges the energy stored in a capacitor for the spark gaps.
3. Transistor oscillator. Continuous or keyed pulses for the spark gap are produced by a transistor oscillator.

Fig. 6-18 illustrates the energy storage system. Transistors Q1 and Q2, and transformer T1 form a saturating-core square-wave inverter that delivers over 160 d-c volts into filter capacitor C1. Capacitor C2 charges to double this voltage through the resonant charging action of C2, choke L1, and diode CR1. When the auto breaker points open, SCR1 is triggered by current from the battery charging C4. At this point capacitor C2 is connected across the coil primary winding, and a high voltage is induced in the coil secondary by transformer action. This high voltage pulse is fed to the appropriate spark plug by the regular auto distributor.

Because capacitor C2 and the primary inductance of the ignition coil form a second oscillatory circuit, capacitor C2 overswings in voltage; this reverse voltage turns off the SCR. Any excess energy remaining in C2 is then fed back to charge C2 in the forward direction via bypass diode CR2. R2 and C3 limit the rate of for-

103

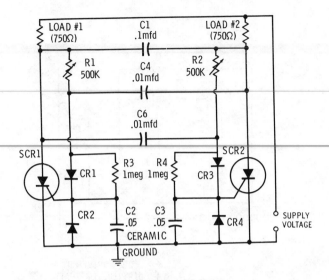

Fig. 6-20. Astable multivibrator.

ward voltage across the SCR to within its dv/dt ratings. When the breaker points close next, C4 is discharged through R4 in readiness for the next cycle. A relatively long discharge time constant is provided for C4 to lessen the possibility of the SCR retriggering due to point bounce. Resistor R1 and diode CR3 further inhibit false triggering by providing a negative gate bias to SCR1 whenever charging current is flowing from the d-c supply to charge C2.

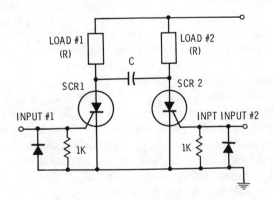

Fig. 6-21. Free-running multivibrator.

This circuit will deliver approximately 23-kv output from a 12.6-volt input, and will operate succeessfully down to a 7-volt input. Output voltage is essentially constant up to approximately 5500 rpm with a V8 four-stroke gasoline engine.

For completely static operation, the standard auto contact points may be replaced by the circuit of Fig. 6-19. The magnetic pickup used to generate the SCR trigger pulses is a standard item; the pickup output is amplified and differentiated before being applied to the SCR gate.

MULTIVIBRATORS

Various multivibrator configurations are possible with the SCR, one of which is shown in Fig. 6-20. To understand the operation of the circuit, consider that SCR1 is conducting load current and SCR2 is blocking. The anode-cathode voltage drop of SCR1 is very low, so the supply voltage appears across load No. 1. Under these conditions C1 charges up to full supply voltage. Since C6 in series with R2 is connected across C1, it will also charge. When the positive voltage developed on C6 reaches the gate voltage required to trigger SCR2 (plus the diode drop of CR3), SCR2 will trigger into conduction. When SCR2 is triggered, the positively charged plate of C1 is suddenly connected to ground through SCR2, making the other plate of C1 negative with respect to ground. Since the latter is tied to the anode of SCR1, this controlled rectifier becomes reverse biased and turns off.

While SCR2 conducts, C1 charges to full supply voltage (but the opposite polarity). C4 also charges, triggering SCR1 into conduction as C6 did SCR2. The charge on C1 now makes the anode of SCR2 negative and cuts it off.

The conduction period of each SCR can be varied independently by adjustment of R1 and R2. By increasing the capacitance of timing capacitors C4 and C6 above that shown, the circuit can be made to operate at very low frequencies. It is then suitable for use as a high-voltage flasher by substituting lamps for loads 1 and 2.

Fig. 6-21 shows another multivibrator. Here input No. 1 energizes load No. 1, and input No. 2 energizes load No. 2. Capacitor C commutates the SCR's, turning off each as the other fires.

Fig. 6-22 shows a one-shot multivibrator where the input triggers the SCR and energizes the load. The load voltage in turn

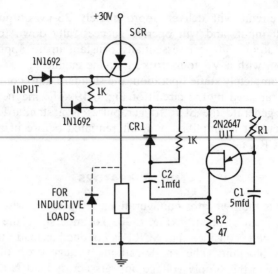

Fig. 6-22. One-shot multivibrator.

energizes the unijunction timer. When the UJT fires, a pulse across R2 is coupled to the SCR cathode through CR1 and C2, lifting it momentarily above the supply voltage. This reverse bias turns off the SCR. Thus, a trigger pulse turns on the SCR for a length of time determined by R1. The SCR turns off by itself, and remains off until there is another input.

7

Related Switching Devices

The SCR is only one of a family of four-layer, or pnpn, semiconductor devices, though it is probably the one with the widest applications at the present time. All of these units consist of n-type and p-type silicon in alternate layers. Fig. 7-1 shows the basic construction and terminology that is used.

One classification of pnpn semiconductors is by the number of leads they have, which is the same as the number of layers to which connections can be made. Under this system they can be arranged as follows:

    2 leads—4 layer diode (Shockley diode)
    3 leads—silicon controlled rectifiers (SCR)
           gate turn-off switch (GTO)
    4 leads—silicon controlled switch (SCS)

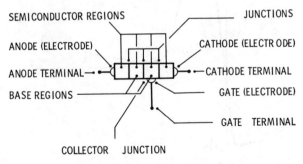

Fig. 7-1. Structure of pnpn devices.

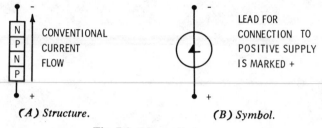

| (A) Structure. | (B) Symbol. |

Fig. 7-2. 4-layer diode.

FOUR-LAYER DIODE

A 4-layer pnpn device with leads (connections) to only the end layers is known as a 4-layer, or Shockley, diode. It has special properties as a switching device. Produced from single-crystal silicon, the four layers are obtained by the controlled diffusion of suitable impurities. Fig. 7-2 is a diagram of the construction of the 4-layer diode and the schematic representation. The symbol for the Shockley 4-layer diode is a modified 4. The slant line of the 4 indicates the forward direction of current passing through the device when it is in the on state.

Characteristics of the 4-layer diode can be seen from Fig. 7-3. This device has two stable states; one is an off or open-circuit

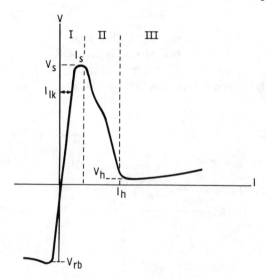

Fig. 7-3. Characteristic curve.

condition in which it acts as a high value of resistance in the 10- to 1,000-megohms range and the other is an on or low-resistance state in which it acts almost as a short circuit. The off state is region I, and the on state is region III as shown in Fig. 7-3. This two-terminal device may be considered as a pnp and npn transistor tied together in a single unit, similar to the SCR. At the proper applied voltage the center junction breaks down, and charged carriers flow. Thus the device may be used as a switch to turn on the applied voltage when the voltage exceeds the switching value.

The 4-layer diode will turn off when the current through it is reduced below holding current, the speed of turn-off depending on circuit conditions. In a typical sawtooth oscillator, for example, the device turns off when the current drops below the holding current, although there is still voltage applied to it. This will take about 1 microsecond. If, by an inductive transient or other means, the voltage across the diode is reversed when it switches, the turn-off time may be reduced appreciably.

In its off condition, the 4-layer diode may be considered as a capacitance and a large resistance in parallel. This capacitance, which is similar to the collector capacitance of a normal transistor, has a value that depends on the actual voltage across the device. In its on condition, the 4-layer diode has such a low resistance that capacitive effects may be ignored. However, it is necessary to charge this capacitor as well as to inject current carriers into the device in the course of switching. This requires energy which must be furnished by either the trigger pulse or circuit elements provided for this purpose.

Because the switching properties of a 4-layer diode closely approach those of the ideal switch, it is finding applications in many fields. In addition to its advantages as a semiconductor— small size and no moving parts—it provides the unusual combination of power handling ability and fast switching. Some of its present applications include pulse generators and amplifiers, oscillators, relay alarm circuits, ring counters, detonator firing circuits, magnetron and sonar pulsing, telephone switching, and driving magnetic cores of computers.

A load limiting resistor or some load impedance is placed in series with the 4-layer diode to prevent it from passing excessive current in the on state. Since the resistance of the device decreases with increasing current (to substantially less than 1 ohm

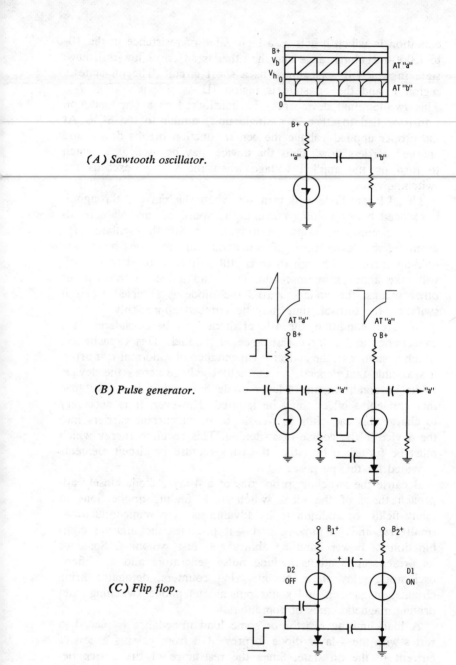

(A) Sawtooth oscillator.

(B) Pulse generator.

(C) Flip flop.

Fig. 7-4. Circuits using 4-layer diodes.

at high pulse currents), it can be destroyed unless the load current is limited.

Some circuits for the 4-layer diode are shown in Fig. 7-4. One of the simplest applications of the diode is as the active element in a sawtooth generator, as illustrated in Fig. 7-4A. In addition to the diode, only two resistors and a single capacitor are needed. Two typical pulse-generator circuits are shown in Fig. 7-4B. A simple pulse generator with low input impedance and a triggered pulse generator with high input impedance are shown. The flip-flop in Fig. 7-4C may be a stable, monostable, or bistable depending on the value of the resistors and the supply voltage.

GATE TURN-OFF SWITCH

The conventional SCR is turned on by a positive current pulse at its gate. In the usual circuit the only way it can be turned off is by removing or reversing the anode voltage; however, it is possible to turn off an SCR by means of a negative gate signal if the anode-to-cathode current is very small at the time; low-powered SCR's have been used this way in practical circuits. They behave like conventional SCR's during turn-on and conduction; then a negative charge (current pulse) introduced at the gate

Courtesy Texas Instruments Incorporated

Fig. 7-5. Gate turn-off switches.

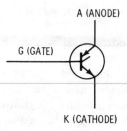

A (ANODE)

G (GATE)

K (CATHODE)

Fig. 7-6. Symbol for GTO.

terminal cancels the charge caused by the load current, and the devices turn off.

The GTO (gate turn-off switch) is a new type of power device operating like the low-power SCR's (Fig. 7-5). Units are available that can switch 5 amps at 400 volts, using a positive gate pulse to turn them on and a negative gate pulse to turn them off. They also turn off when the supply voltage is removed, as does the regular SCR. Turn-off current gain is around ten, but this low current gain in no way limits the utility of this SCR, since considerable power gain is achieved during turn-off. The turn-off voltage has to be only 3 volts or so in order to switch 400 volts. The turn-off signal has to exist for only a small part of a millisecond. The usual method of turn-off is to discharge a capacitor into the gate in order to provide the required high-current pulse. The GTO may also be turned off by direct connection to a low-impedance negative voltage using a transistor.

The GTO is particularly useful in d-c circuits, since SCR turn-off is no problem using a-c power. It can switch very rapidly —cycling up to one-hundred-thousand times a second. There is no tendency to create radio interference with this rapid switching.

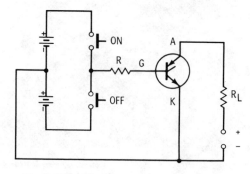

Fig. 7-7. Latching relay—push on, push off.

The symbol for the gate turn-off switch is shown in Fig. 7-6. Electron flow in the load circuit is from cathode to anode, and it is controlled by positive or negative pulses applied between the gate and the cathode terminals.

The fabrication of gate turn-off switches is more difficult than ordinary SCR's so they probably never can approach the price of the economy SCR's. However, simplification and the new circuit possibilities can reduce equipment cost in some cases when GTO's are used to replace SCR's.

Fig. 7-7 shows the operation of the GTO as a latching relay. Action is as follows:

1. When both switches are open, the GTO is off.
2. Depressing the on pushbutton applies a positive signal to the gate, triggering the device on. Conduction continues after the pushbutton is released.
3. Depressing the pushbutton applies a negative signal to the gate. This turns the GTO off.

In Fig. 7-8 the GTO is on with the switch open and off with the switch closed. With the switch open capacitor C1 charges toward the supply voltage, triggering the GTO on when the voltage across the capacitor reaches a sufficient value. Closing switch S1 discharges the capacitor through R2, reversing the current in the gate-cathode circuit. This turns the GTO off.

OTHER SCR'S

In addition to the conventional SCR's described previously in this book, there are several special-purpose units. They are

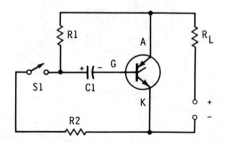

Fig. 7-8. Latching relay—single pushbutton.

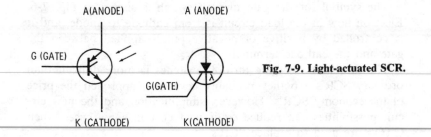

Fig. 7-9. Light-actuated SCR.

generally similar to those discussed but have some additional properties that increase their usefulness in certain circuits. Two of these are the light-activated SCR (LASCR) and the avalanche-breakdown SCR.

Light-Actuated SCR

The light-actuated triode switch (SCR) is also known as the LASCR (General Electric) and the Photran (Solid State Products). As with many pnpn devices there are several possible symbols for this device, but the two commonly used are shown in Fig. 7-9. This special type of SCR can be turned on by light falling on the junction in addition to the normal triggering methods for SCR's. Physical construction of the LASCR can be seen in Fig. 7-10.

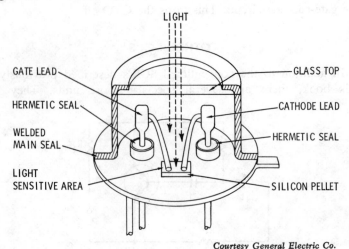

Courtesy General Electric Co.

Fig. 7-10. Physical construction of a LASCR.

The time required to turn the device on is directly related to the light intensity used for triggering. When the light intensity is at the minimum required level, the turn on time is typically 10 microseconds. If desired, this time can be reduced to less than one microsecond by an increase in the light intensity. The turn-off time, typically 30 microseconds, is primarily controlled by the recovery time of the device.

The LASCR is responsive to a wider range of light wavelengths than the human eye. While it can be triggered by all visible light, it is also sensitive to infrared radiation and, to a lesser extent, ultraviolet.

Once light has triggered the device on, it will remain on indefinitely—until electrically turned off by opening the anode circuit or by reducing the anode current to zero (just the same as other SCR's). The device can be said to remember a light pulse, a property that can be used in many applications to provide electro-optical control. Logic systems can be designed using light-actuated SCR's.

The light intensity required to trigger the unit can be set electrically by changing its gate bias current. The bias-control property allows simple electrical gating. With a high bias level the device can be made nonresponsive to light, then by reducing the bias it can be made to react normally. Electrical triggering can be used in addition to optical triggering.

Consider a simple circuit (Fig. 7-11) where a negative or positive pulse is desired as an output when light is or is not present. In counting, sorting, timing, indexing, and programming, a discrete pulse output for each interruption of light at the photo-cell input is often desired. Pulse-generator circuits can also be designed to provide a single pulse each time a light beam has been removed and then is subsequently reapplied to the cell.

There are two modes of operation. One is for light to fall continuously on the cell; then the device conducts a small amount of current (under 100 ua) continuously through R1 that prevents C1 from charging. When the light is temporarily removed from the unit, it ceases conduction; capacitor C will charge to the supply voltage through R1. When light is subsequently applied, the device is triggered on, and C1 discharges, giving an output pulse.

An alternate mode of operation is by light impulse. Here light is normally not present on the cell, so C1 is fully charged. When

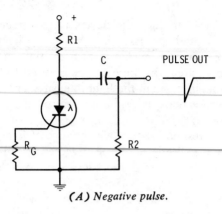

(A) Negative pulse.

(B) Positive pulse.

Fig. 7-11. Light-triggered, pulse-output circuits.

a light impulse occurs, the LASCR conducts, discharging C1 and putting a pulse on the output line. C1 recharges after the light impulse terminates. In either of these modes of operation the amplitude and width of the output pulse are set by circuit values and are independent of light intensity.

The light-actuated SCR can be operated from a-c as well as d-c power sources. When alternating current is used, the device will block during the positive half-cycle if it has not been triggered by light, and will conduct if it has been triggered by light. During the negative half-cycle the unit acts as a blocking diode regardless of whether light falls on it or not. If the device has been conducting during a positive half-cycle, it will automatically drop

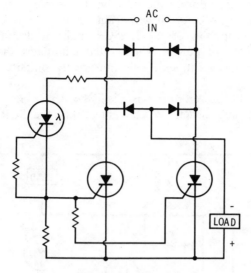

(A) Triggered by light.

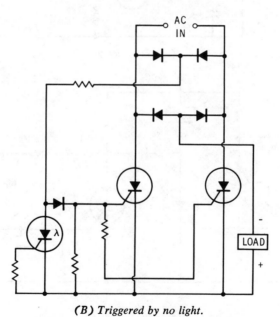

(B) Triggered by no light.

Courtesy Solid State Products, Inc.
Fig. 7-12. Light-triggered power switches.

out of conduction during the negative half-cycle. It must be re-triggered with light before it will again conduct on a positive half-cycle. The properties of the LASCR make it desirable to use a-c instead of d-c power, which often eliminates the need for separate d-c power supplies. This can greatly simplify many control systems.

Where a d-c power source is used, the device acts as a light-actuated latching switch. When light strikes the SCR, power is

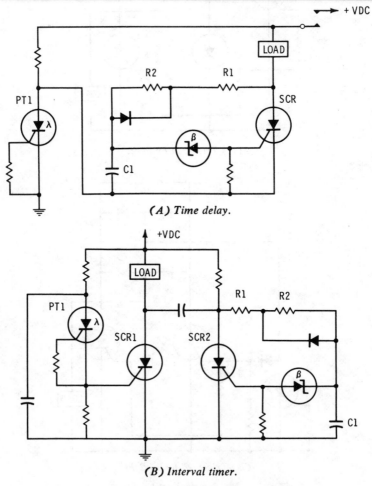

(A) Time delay.

(B) Interval timer.

Courtesy Solid State Products, Inc.
Fig. 7-13. Light-activated SCR circuits.

applied to the load. The device will continue to conduct after the light has been removed. Load power in this case is turned off by a reset switch or a similar device.

In many control-systems applications it is necessary to supply relatively large amounts of power to a load from photocell inputs. In these cases a light-actuated SCR can be used to excite a power relay, using a simple control circuit. Two circuits for switching large amount of power are shown in Fig. 7-12; both the circuits provide full-wave d-c output to the load. In Fig. 7-12A full output is supplied when light is present. There is no output when light is removed. In Fig. 7-12B the opposite action is achieved; this circuit provides power to the load when light is removed and

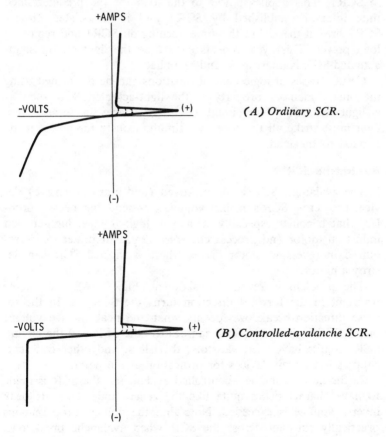

(A) Ordinary SCR.

(B) Controlled-avalanche SCR.

Fig. 7-14. Characteristic curves.

no power when light is present. In both of these circuits the light-actuated SCR is used to control the gate signal to a pair of regular SCR's. The light switch can supply the necessary gate firing power to all SCR's, including those with ratings up to 70 amperes.

Fig. 7-13 shows two circuits for the control of power to a d-c load. Fig. 7-13A is a light-actuated time-delay circuit. When light is applied to PT1, C1 begins charging through R1 and R2. After a predetermined time interval, SCR1 fires, applying power to the load. The circuit is reset by interrupting the d-c power source.

Fig. 7-13B is a light-actuated interval timer. The pulse generator incorporating PT1 is used to provide a gate firing pulse to SCR1. This applies power to the load for the predetermined time interval established by SCR2 and its associated circuit. SCR2 fires at the end of this time, turning off SCR1 and removing load power. This cycle repeats each time the light on the light-actuated SCR is interrupted and reapplied.

Certain types of logic control functions can be performed using the binary memory property of the light-actuated SCR such as a light-actuated AND circuit of three devices in series. Here light must strike all three devices simultaneously for power to be applied to the load.

Avalanche SCR

The avalanche SCR is an improved (and more expensive) device. Protecting SCR's against voltage transients has been a problem that becomes especially critical in high-voltage, high-current industrial motor and process controls. Transient protection is required in reversing motor drives where a shorted SCR can destroy a motor.

The problem is reverse breakdown (Fig. 7-14). A voltage transient in the forward direction turns the SCR on. In the reverse direction breakdown occurs when the peak inverse voltage of the SCR is exceeded. This can destroy the SCR and the circuit. SCR circuits have used varistors, thyristors, and other transient-suppression circuit devices for protection at the point.

In the new technique—controlled avalanche—the SCR is made to have characteristics quite like the zener diode when its peak inverse voltage is exceeded. Note that the voltage drop remains practically constant across the SCR when avalanche breakdown occurs. Instead of shorting and allowing unlimited voltage across the load, the avalanche SCR continues to have a voltage drop across itself. A transient that could do circuit damage is absorbed by the SCR and dissipated as heat without damage.

Temperature creates the problem at the breakdown point. If the current density (current per square inch) gets too high, the SCR will actually melt and, of course, cease to function. A non-uniform junction of semiconductor materials will cause a hot spot that carries heavy current, while the rest of the junction carries none (or very little). The resultant high current density will destroy the junction at this point.

The uniform junction breaks down uniformly since the same current is now distributed over the entire surface. The resultant current density is very low. Although the same amount of heat is produced in both cases, the uniform junction temperature remains at a safe level.

Reverse breakdown first takes place in the ordinary SCR in one small region, damaging the device. In the controlled-avalanche SCR's, reverse breakdown is uniform across the entire junction, preventing damaging local temperature rise. The reverse breakdown of a regular and a controlled-avalanche SCR is shown in Fig. 7-14.

Controlled avalanche results from careful SCR design and improved control of the SCR properties during fabrication. Beveling the silicon structure produces the desired uniform breakdown. Passivating the silicon materials by coating with oxide or nitride also prevents edge or surface contamination.

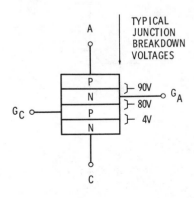

Fig. 7-15. Structure of an SCS.

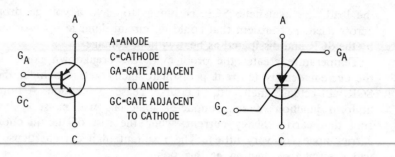

A = ANODE
C = CATHODE
GA = GATE ADJACENT
        TO ANODE
GC = GATE ADJACENT
        TO CATHODE

Fig. 7-16. Symbols for SCS's.

V_{ON}	V_{OFF}	R_A	R_G	R_C
+1	-1	100	470	10K
+1	-1	100	100	3.3K
+1	-1	100	0	1K
+1	-3	100	0	330

V_{ON}	V_{OFF}	R_A
+.6	0	10K
+.6	-1	3.3K
+.6	-4	1K

(A) In-phase output.   *(B) Out-of-phase output.*

Courtesy General Electric Co.

Fig. 7-17. Bistable memory circuits.

SILICON CONTROLLED SWITCH

The silicon controlled switch (SCS) is a four-layer semiconductor (pnpn) with leads attached to each layer. Structure of the SCS is shown in Fig. 7-15. Two commonly used symbols are shown in Fig. 7-16. Like an SCR the switching action takes place between the cathode and the anode. To turn the SCR on a positive triggering signal is applied to the gate-to-cathode junction. To turn it off a negative trigger is applied to the gate-to-anode junction.

The SCR is essentially a small-signal device. In typical operation it is able to handle currents of approximately 50 milliamperes at about 60 volts. Applications include tone generators, pulse generators, computer circuitry, and control indicators.

Fig. 7-17 shows the use of a single SCS as a bistable memory element. In Fig. 7-17A the load is in the cathode and the output is in phase with the input. Four different values of load resistance are given, and with each associated values for R_A, R_G, and the on and off pulses are provided.

The circuit in Fig. 7-17B has a load in the anode so the output is out of phase with the input. For different values of the load resistor, various values of off and on voltages are shown.

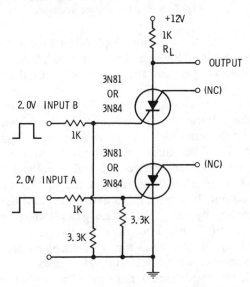

Courtesy General Electric Co.

Fig. 7-18. Pulse-coincidence detector.

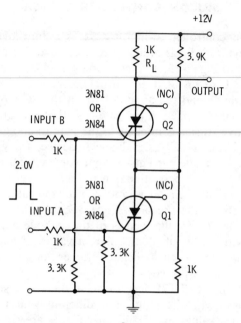

Courtesy General Electric Co.
Fig. 7-19. Pulse-sequence detector.

A pulse-coincidence detector (Fig. 7-18) uses a pair of silicon controlled switches. Although there are two gates shown in this circuit, the cathode gate and the anode gate, only the cathode gate is used.

The d-c supply here is 12 volts; each of the two inputs is a 2.0-volt pulse. Unless there is an input at A and an input at B that occur at the same time, there will be no voltage across the load resistor R_L. The input pulses must be at least 2 volts in amplitude and should be between 2 and 3 volts. Less than one microsecond of overlap is enough to trigger the two SCR's to provide an output. It is possible to detect the coincidence of negative input pulses by using the anode gates (which are not connected in this figure) instead of the cathode gates.

The circuit in Fig. 7-19 uses a pair of silicon controlled switches in a pulse-sequence detector circuit. Here also the cathode gate is used while the anode gate is not used. This circuit has a 12-volt d-c supply. The first input pulse to B after there is an input at A will provide a current through R_L; the output is the voltage drop across this resistance. A resistance divider network is connected between the two switches Q1 and Q2 so that there is a current supply for Q1 after a pulse input to the cathode gate of Q1 triggers this switch into conduction. This divider network also prevents an input from B from triggering switch Q2 until after switch Q1 conducts. Thus, this is a pulse sequence circuit.

Index